D1060943

The Physiological Basis of Athletic Records

Publication Number 712
AMERICAN LECTURE SERIES®

A Monograph in
The BANNERSTONE DIVISION *of*
AMERICAN LECTURES IN SPORTSMEDICINE

Edited by
ERNST JOKL, M.D.
University of Kentucky
Lexington, Kentucky

The Physiological Basis of Athletic Records

By

ERNST JOKL and PETER JOKL
University of Kentucky
Lexington, Kentucky

Published for and on behalf of

Research Committee
International Council of Sport & Physical Education
UNESCO

CHARLES C THOMAS · PUBLISHER
Springfield · Illinois · U.S.A.

Published and Distributed Throughout the World by
CHARLES C THOMAS • PUBLISHER
BANNERSTONE HOUSE
301-327 East Lawrence Avenue, Springfield, Illinois, U.S.A.
NATCHEZ PLANTATION HOUSE
735 North Atlantic Boulevard, Fort Lauderdale, Florida, U.S.A.

Library of Congress Catalog Card Number: 68-13762

Printed in the United States of America
H-2

To Philip Noel Baker

PREFACE

THIS MONOGRAPH, the ninth in the series on sportsmedicine published by Charles C Thomas, deals with *The Physiological Basis of Athletic Records*. The title corresponds to that of Professor A. V. Hill's Presidential Address to the Physiological Section of the British Association for the Advancement of Science at its ninety-third meeting in Southampton in 1925, which established *physiology of exercise* as a division of physiology. In the intervening years much new information has become available. The time seems therefore appropriate to review the evidence, including results not only of physiological and clinical but also of relevant psychological, sociological, and esthetic studies.

Research on the athletic record deserves the attention of the biophysicist, the biochemist, the physician as well as the statistician. Assessment of scope and limitations of human efficiency raises issues of categorical importance to anthropology in its widest sense in that maximal performance reflects nature and extent of the integrative function of the nervous system and with it of man's capacity to "materialize" ideas and images. In the maximal human performance "the coexistence of energy and mind," of which Sherrington wrote in his book *Man on His Nature,* manifests itself in a new light. For this reason alone the significance of the theme of this monograph transcends the realms of physiology and medicine.

We are indebted to Professors M. J. Karvonen of Helsinki, Finland, A. H. Frucht of Berlin-Lichtenberg, East-Germany, J. M. Tanner of London, England, and Frank Kobes, West Point, N. Y. as well as to the other authors mentioned in the text who gave permission to reproduce diagrams from their publications, the first two written jointly with us. Our sincere thanks are due to the Deutsche Presse Agentur (D.P.A.), Frankfurt, Germany, who have kindly placed at our disposal the excellent photographs from the 1964 Olympic Games in Tokyo. Dr. Elisabeth Esser has rendered valuable service with the preparation of the manuscript.

ERNST AND PETER JOKL

CONTENTS

ILLUSTRATIONS

TABLES

The Physiological Basis of Athletic Records

Chapter I

HISTORICAL NOTES

MEASUREMENTS OF athletic performances were first recorded in England. For example, data are available for the long jump since 1866 (Table I). During the preceding centuries the only criterion of an athlete's efficiency was his ability to prevail against his opponents. Nobody could say how a given feat compared with those of others who competed elsewhere. The entire period prior to the second half of the nineteenth century must therefore be looked upon as the prehistoric era of the modern sports movement.

In the last one hundred years record performances in the long

TABLE I

DEVELOPMENT OF THE WORLD RECORD IN BROAD JUMPING (1866- TO DATE)

6.00 m	Fitzherbert R.	England	1866
6.01 m	Mitchell R. J. C.	England	1868
6.09 m	Mitchell R. J. C.	England	1870
6.20 m	Little	England	1870
6.20 m	Mitchell R. J. C.	England	1871
6.89 m	Davies E. J.	England	1872
6.91 m	Baddeley E.	England	1878
6.99 m	Davin P.	England	1881
7.02 m	Parsons J. W.	England	1883
7.06 m	Schifferstein V. E.	U.S.A.	1888
7.09 m	Ford M. W.	U.S.A.	1888
7.09 m	Copland A. F.	U.S.A.	1890
7.13 m	Reber C. S.	U.S.A.	1893
7.18 m	Fry C. B.	England	1893
7.21 m	Rosengrave N. M.	Australia	1896
7.23 m	Jones H. A.	U.S.A.	1897
7.47 m	Newburn	England	1898
7.50 m	Prinstein M.	U.S.A.	1900
7.61 m	O'Connor P.	Ireland	1901
7.70 m	Gourdin E.	U.S.A.	1921
7.77 m	Le Gendre R.	U.S.A.	1924
7.89 m	De Hart Hubbard W.	U.S.A.	1925
7.90 m	Hamm E.	U.S.A.	1928
7.93 m	Cator S.	Haiti	1928
7.98 m	Nambu Ch.	Japan	1931
8.13 m	Owens J.	U.S.A.	1935
8.21 m	Boston	U.S.A.	1960
8.24 m	Boston	U.S.A.	1961
8.28 m	Boston	U.S.A.	1961
8.31 m	Ter-Owanesjan	U.S.S.R.	1962
8.34 m	Boston	U.S.A.	1964

jump for men have increased from under 6.00 to 8.35 meters; in the ski jump from 23 to 154 meters; in the shot put from 10.67 to 21.78 meters; in the 5,000-meter race from 16.53.0 to 13.16.6 minutes. Debbie Meyer's free style swimming world record over the 1,500-meter (17.50.2 minutes) is 1.28.3 minutes better than the winning time of 19.18.5 minutes in the men's final at the Olympic Games in London in 1948.

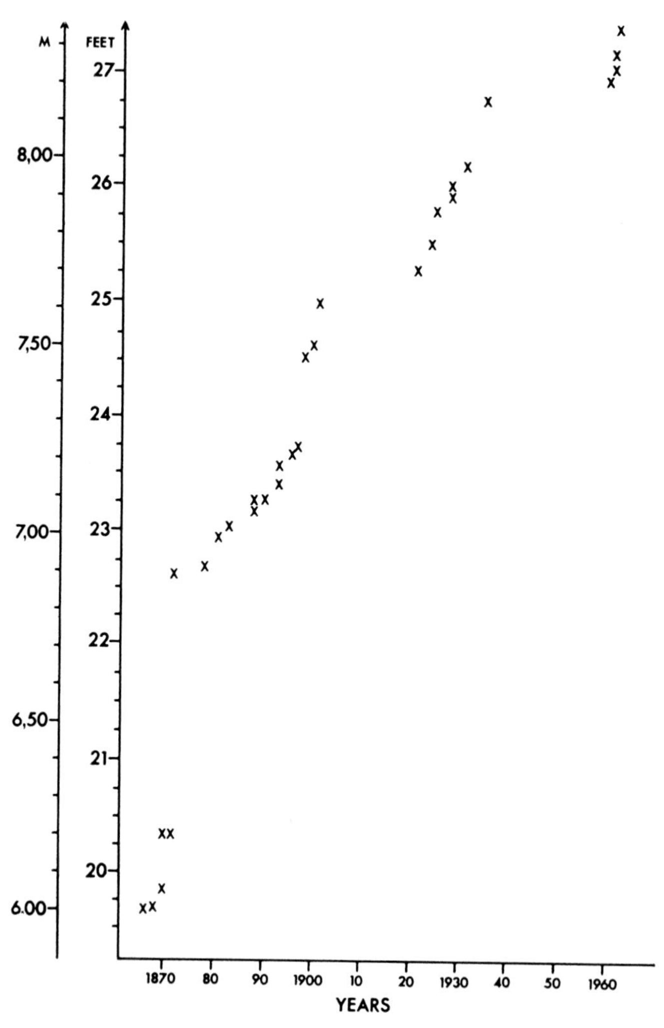

FIGURE 1. Scatter diagram showing improvement of world record in long jump since 1866.

Scatter diagrams showing the growth of athletic records reveal a seemingly irregular distribution (Fig. 1). Sudden improvements of performance in the long jump occurred around 1872, 1896 and 1900 while between 1901 and 1921 and between 1935 and 1960 no changes took place. Figure 2 depicts the mean trend of improvement as well as periodic fluctuations during the period under analysis.

Curves showing similar growth patterns have been constructed for other athletic events, for men as well as for women. Figure 3 shows the development of the 400-meter free style swimming Olympic record. Debbie Meyer's world record established during the A.A.U. Swimming and Diving Championships in 1967 (4 min. 29 sec.) surpasses the winning time of Mr. J. Boiteux (4 min. 30.7 sec.) at the 1952 Olympic Games in Helsinki, Finland. It is a matter of great physio-

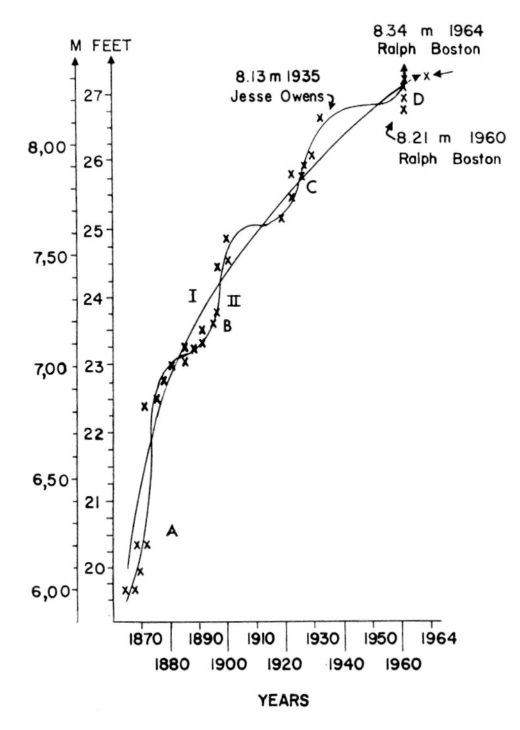

FIGURE 2. Growth trend of long jump world record since 1866. (*I*) shows mean improvement, (*II*) periodic fluctuations. Jesse Owen's world record of 1935 remained unchallenged for 25 years. The arrows at the end of curves (*I*) and (*II*) point in different directions. The predictive validity of curve (*I*) was corroborated by Boston's 1964 world record of 8.34 meters.

logical interest that in other athletic disciplines the advancement of women's records followed different patterns, e.g. Mary Rand's world record in the long jump of 6.76 meters established at Tokyo in 1964 is equivalent only to the men's best performance in the same event of 1875. This is due to the fact first recognized by A. V. Hill (1925)

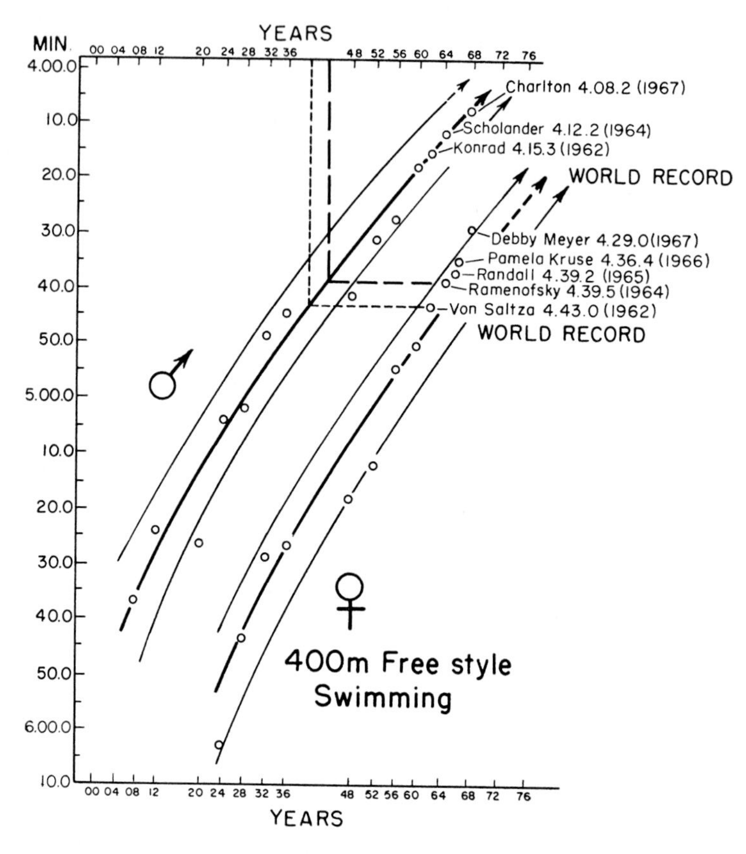

FIGURE 3. Growth curves of world records in 400-meter free style swimming, for men and women, since 1908 and 1924, respectively. Both families of curves were computed from the available data until 1960 and extrapolated for 1968. The subsequent record times complied precisely with their computed predictions. In 1965 Martha Randall established a world record of 4.38.0 min. which was again improved in 1966 by Pamela Kruse to 4.36.4. At the A.A.U. Swimming and Diving Championships in Philadelphia in 1967, 14 year old Debbie Meyer swam a best-ever time of 4.29.0. Corresponding performance improvements have occurred in all other athletic disciplines. (Debbie Meyer's winning time at the 'Pre-Olympic Games' in Mexico City on Oct. 27, 1967 was 4.45.1 min.)

TABLE II

SHOTPUT WORLD RECORDS FROM 1870-1965 AND OLYMPIC PERFORMANCES FROM 1896-1964

		meters
1870-1880	Unknown	10.67-12.19
1887	G. Gray (Canada)	13.38
1893	G. Gray (Canada)	14.32
1897	D. Horgan (Ireland)	14.68
1904	R. Rose (U.S.A.)	14.81
1904	D. Horgan (Ireland)	14.88
1905	W. Coe (U.S.A.)	15.09
1907	R. Rose (U.S.A.)	15.12
1908	R. Rose (U.S.A.)	15.19
1909	R. Rose (U.S.A.)	15.54
1928	E. Hirschfeld (Germany)	15.79
1928	J. Kuck (U.S.A.)	15.87
1928	E. Hirschfeld (Germany)	16.04
1932	Z. Heljasz (Poland)	16.05
1932	L. Sexton (U.S.A.)	16.16
1932	F. Douda (Czechoslovakia)	16.20
1934	J. Lyman (U.S.A.)	16.48
1934	J. Torrance (U.S.A.)	16.80
1934	J. Torrance (U.S.A.)	16.89
1934	J. Torrance (U.S.A.)	17.40
1948	C. Fonville (U.S.A.)	17.68
1949	J. Fuchs (U.S.A.)	17.79
1950	J. Fuchs (U.S.A.)	17.81
1950	J. Fuchs (U.S.A.)	17.89
1950	J. Fuchs (U.S.A.)	17.91
1950	J. Fuchs (U.S.A.)	17.95
1953	P. O'Brien (U.S.A.)	18.00
1953	P. O'Brien (U.S.A.)	18.04
1954	P. O'Brien (U.S.A.)	18.23
1954	P. O'Brien (U.S.A.)	18.42
1954	P. O'Brien (U.S.A.)	18.43
1954	P. O'Brien (U.S.A.)	18.54
1956	P. O'Brien (U.S.A.)	18.61
1956	P. O'Brien (U.S.A.)	18.69
1956	P. O'Brien (U.S.A.)	18.70
1956	P. O'Brien (U.S.A.)	19.05
1956	P. O'Brien (U.S.A.)	19.25
1959	P. O'Brien (U.S.A.)	19.30
1960	D. Long (U.S.A.)	19.67
1960	B. Nieder (U.S.A.)	19.99
1960	B. Nieder (U.S.A.)	20.06
1962	D. Long (U.S.A.)	20.08
1964	D. Long (U.S.A.)	20.68
1965	R. Matson (U.S.A.)	20.70
1965	R. Matson (U.S.A.)	21.51
1967	R. Matson (U.S.A.)	21.78

OLYMPIC WINNERS

1896	R. Garrett (U.S.A.)		(OR)	11.22
1900	R. Sheldon (U.S.A.)		(OR)	14.10
1904	R. Rose (U.S.A.)	(WR)	(OR)	14.81
1908	R. Rose (U.S.A.)			14.21
1912	P. McDonald (U.S.A.)		(OR)	15.34
1920	V. Porhola (Finland)			14.81
1924	C. Houser (U.S.A.)			14.99
1928	J. Kuck (U.S.A.)	(WR)	(OR)	15.87
1932	L. Sexton (U.S.A.)		(OR)	16.00
1936	H. Woelcke (Germany)		(OR)	16.20
1948	W. Thompson (U.S.A.)		(OR)	17.12
1952	P. O'Brien (U.S.A.)		(OR)	17.41
1956	P. O'Brien (U.S.A.)		(OR)	18.57
1960	B. Nieder (U.S.A.)		(OR)	19.68
1964	D. Long (U.S.A.)		(OR)	20.33

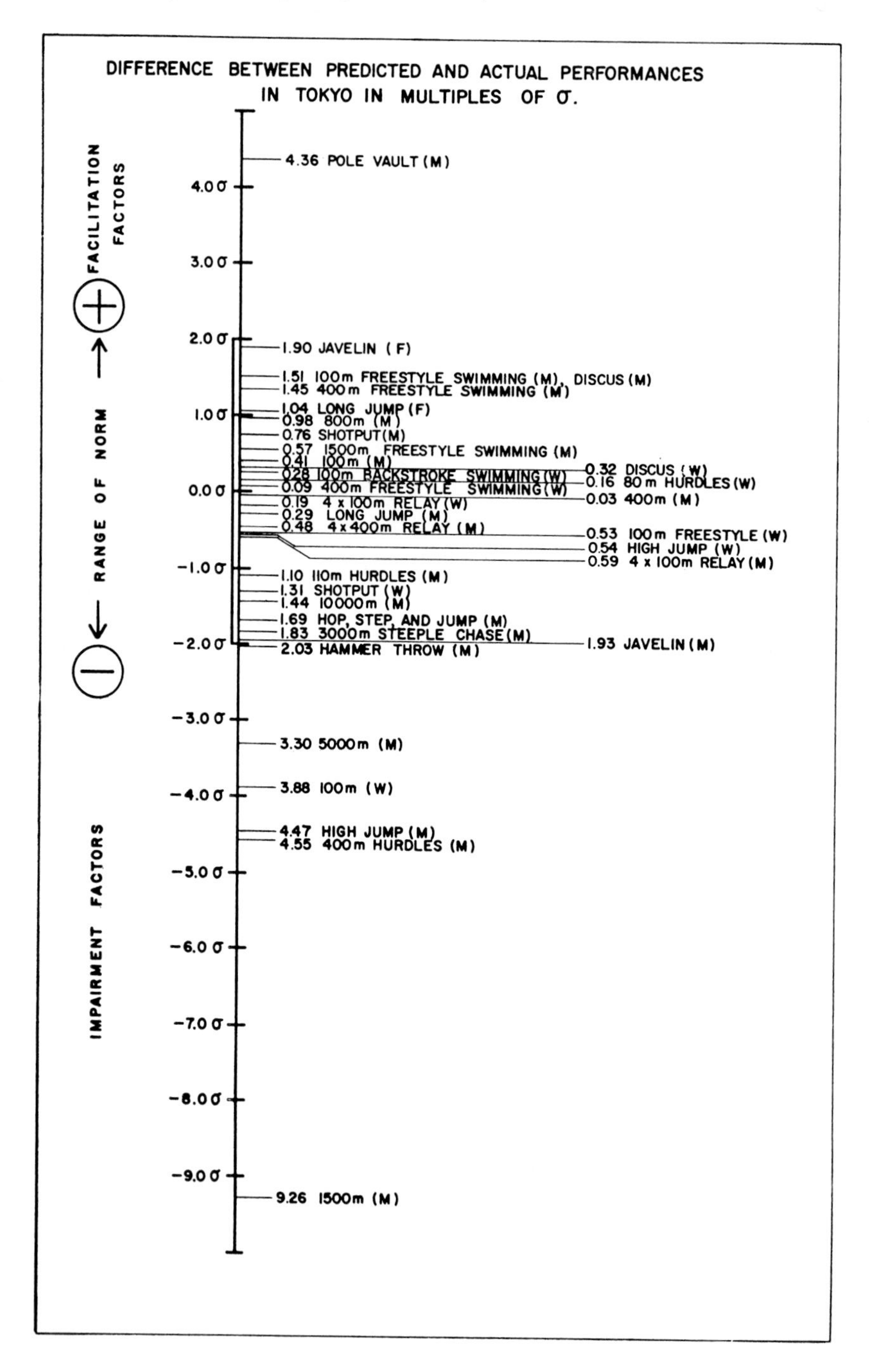
DIFFERENCE BETWEEN PREDICTED AND ACTUAL PERFORMANCES IN TOKYO IN MULTIPLES OF σ.
FACILITATION FACTORS
RANGE OF NORM
IMPAIRMENT FACTORS
4.0σ
3.0σ
2.0σ
1.0σ
0.0σ
-1.0σ
-2.0σ
-3.0σ
-4.0σ
-5.0σ
-6.0σ
-7.0σ
-8.0σ
-9.0σ
4.36 POLE VAULT (M)
1.90 JAVELIN (F)
1.51 100m FREESTYLE SWIMMING (M), DISCUS (M)
1.45 400m FREESTYLE SWIMMING (M)
1.04 LONG JUMP (F)
0.98 800m (M)
0.76 SHOTPUT (M)
0.57 1500m FREESTYLE SWIMMING (M)
0.41 100m (M)
0.28 100m BACKSTROKE SWIMMING (W)
0.09 400m FREESTYLE SWIMMING (W)
0.32 DISCUS (W)
0.16 80 m HURDLES (W)
0.03 400m (M)
0.19 4 x 100m RELAY (W)
0.29 LONG JUMP (M)
0.48 4 x 400m RELAY (M)
0.53 100m FREESTYLE (W)
0.54 HIGH JUMP (W)
0.59 4 x 100m RELAY (M)
1.10 110m HURDLES (M)
1.31 SHOTPUT (W)
1.44 10000m (M)
1.69 HOP, STEP, AND JUMP (M)
1.83 3000m STEEPLE CHASE (M)
1.93 JAVELIN (M)
2.03 HAMMER THROW (M)
3.30 5000m (M)
3.88 100m (W)
4.47 HIGH JUMP (M)
4.55 400m HURDLES (M)
9.26 1500m (M)

that a woman athlete attaining 80 percent of a man's maximal running speed will reach only 64 percent of his optimal jumping performance.

All growth trends of athletic records can be represented by parabolic curves which possess known mathematical characteristics and can be extrapolated with the result that short-term performance predictions can be based upon them. The reliability of such predictions is shown in Figure 4 in which differences between anticipated and actual results in the swimming and track and field competitions at the Olympic Games in 1964 are plotted in multiples of one standard deviation. The growth pattern of athletic performances can be demonstrated in every performance field. Tables II, III, and IV and Figures 5 and 6 contain detailed evidence. Corresponding gains in physical efficiency have also occurred in the population at large, at least in coun-

---

FIGURE 4. Differences between anticipated and actual results in the swimming and track and field contests at the Olympic games in 1964 are plotted in multiples of one standard deviation. Most results at Tokyo fell within two standard deviations of the calculated means, that is they complied with accepted statistical criteria of validity. The indoor swimming competitions were not subject to climatic disturbances and agreement between computed and measured times was therefore particularly good. Twenty out of 25 track and field events had been correctly predicted, a surprising correspondence considering the sensitivity of all athletic outdoor contests towards extraneous influences. As to the five exceptions, it was known beforehand that the results of the pole vault would be out of line with previous performance developments because of the introduction of the fiberglass pole. Schul's winning time of 13.48.8 min in the 5000-meter track final which was run in heavy rain was nine seconds slower than Kuz's performance in Melbourne in 1956, fifteen seconds slower than our prediction for 1964, the validity of which was subsequently demonstrated by Ron Clarke's world record performances of 13.33.6 min, 13.25.8, and 13.16.6. Climatic conditions contributed to but did not fully explain the "sub-standard" performances in the remaining four Olympic events under reference, *viz.* the 100-meter race for women, the high jump, the 400-meter hurdles and 1500-meter races for men. Prior to 1964, exceptional record performances had been established in these competitions by Wilma Rudolf, Valery Brumel, Glen Davis and Herbert Elliott. The latter's world record of 3:35.6 min in the 1500 meter race in Rome in 1960 was superior to Snel's run of 3:38.1 min in Tokyo in 1964. It remained unsurpassed until July, 1967, when Jim Ryan clocked 3:33.1 min. at Los Angeles, California. Brumel, the world record holder in the high jump, won his event in Tokyo with a leap 10 cm below his best previous performance which had been achieved under incomparably more favorable circumstances.

tries with a tradition in school physical training, such as Switzerland.

Tables V A-C are of considerable interest in that they allow comparisons not only of *individual* top level performances over a period of several years but also of results obtained by representative *samples*: in V-A of the twelve best track and field competitors (men), V-B (women), at Olympic games 1952, 1956, 1960 and 1964, and in V-C of young Swiss military recruits between 1905 and 1960. V-D represents a qualifying list for the 1968 Olympic Games in Mexico City which postulates better performances than those that would have sufficed to win gold medals in 1952 or 1956 (p. 18).

TABLE III

DEVELOPMENT OF THE WORLD RECORD IN THE 5,000-METER RACE (1912- TO DATE)

1912	J. Bouin (France)	15.05.0
1912	H. Kolehmainen (Finland)	14.36.6
1922	P. Nurmi (Finland)	14.35.4
1924	P. Nurmi (Finland)	14.28.2
1932	L. Lethinen (Finland)	14.17.0
1939	T. Maki (Finland)	14.08.8
1942	G. Hagg (Sweden)	13.58.2
1954	E. Zatopek (Czechoslovakia)	13.57.2
1954	W. Kuts (U.S.S.R.)	13.56.6
1954	Ch. Chataway (Great Britain)	13.51.6
1954	W. Kuts (U.S.S.R.)	13.51.2
1955	S. Iharos (Hungary)	13.50.8
1955	W. Kuts (U.S.S.R.)	13.46.8
1955	S. Iharos (Hungary)	13.40.6
1956	G. Pirie (Great Britain)	13.36.8
1957	W. Kuts (U.S.S.R.)	13.35.0
1965	R. Clarke (Australia)	13.33.6
1965	M. Jazy (France)	13.29.0
1965	R. Clarke (Australia)	13.25.8
1966	R. Clarke (Australia)	13.16.6

TABLE IV-A

1897-1967 BOSTON MARATHON WINNERS

	Name, Age	*Time*
1897	James J. McDermott, 25	2:55.10
1898	Ronald J. McDonald, 22	2:42.00
1899	Lawrence Brignolia, 23	2:54.38
1900	James J. Caffrey, 23	2:39.44
1901	James J. Caffrey, 24	2:39.23
1902	Sammy Mellor, Jr., 23	2:43.12
1903	John C. Lorden, 28	2:41.29
1904	Michael Spring, 21	2:38.04
1905	Fred Lorz, 25	2:38.25
1906	Timothy Ford, 18	2:45.45
1907	Tom Longboat, 19	2:24.24

1908	Thomas Morrissey, 20	2:25.43
1909	Henri Renaud, 19	2:53.36
1910	Fred Cameron, 23	2:28.52
1911	Clarence DeMar, 21	2:21.39
1912	Mike Ryan, 23	2:21.18
1913	Fritz Carlson, 29	2:25.14
1914	James Duffy, 24	2:25.01
1915	Edouard Fabre, 28	2:31.41
1916	Arthur Roth, 23	2:27.16
1917	Bill Kennedy, 35	2:28.37
1919	Carl Linder, 29	2:29.13
1920	Peter Trivoulidas, 29	2:29.31
1921	Frank Zuna, 27	2:18.57
1922	Clarence DeMar, 31	2:18.10
1923	Clarence DeMar, 32	2:23.37
1924	Clarence DeMar, 33	2:29.40
1925	Charles Mellor, 31	2:33.00
1926	John C. Miles, 19	2:25.40
1927	Clarence DeMar, 36	2:40.22
1928	Clarence DeMar, 37	2:37.70
1929	John C. Miles, 22	2:33.80
1930	Clarence DeMar, 39	2:34.48
1931	Jimmy Henigan, 39	2:46.45
1932	Paul de Bruyn, 24	2:33.36
1933	Leslie Pawson, 28	2:31.01
1934	Dave Komonen, 35	2:32.53
1935	John A. Kelley, 27	2:32.70
1936	Ellison M. Brown, 22	2:33.40
1937	Walter Young, 24	2:33.20
1938	Leslie Pawson, 33	2:35.34
1939	Ellison M. Brown, 25	2:28.51
1940	Gerard Cote, 26	2:28.28
1941	Leslie Pawson, 36	2:30.38
1942	B. Joseph Smith, 27	2:26.51
1943	Gerard Cote, 28	2:28.25
1944	Gerard Cote, 29	2:31.50
1945	John A. Kelley, 37	2:30.40
1946	Stylianos Kyriakides, 36	2:29.27
1947	Yun Bok Suh, 24	2:25.39
1948	Gerard Cote, 34	2:31.20
1949	K. Gosta Leandersson, 31	2:31.50
1950	Kee Yong Ham, 19	2:32.39
1951	Shigeki Tanaka, 19	2:27.45
1952	Doroteo Flores, 30	2:31.53
1953	Keizo Yamada, 24	2:18.51
1954	Veikko Karvonen, 28	2:20.39
1955	Hideo Hamamura, 26	2:18.22
1956	Antti Viskari, 27	2:14.14
1957	John J. Kelley, 26	2:20.05
1958	Franjo Mihalic, 36	2:25.54
1959	Eino Oksanen, 27	2:22.42
1960	Paavo Kotila, 32	2:20.54
1961	Eino Oksanen, 29	2:23.39
1962	Eino Oksanen, 30	2:23.48
1963	Aurele Vandendriessche, 29	2:18.58
1964	Aurele Vandendriessche, 30	2:19.59
1965	Morio Shigematsu, 24	2:16.33
1966	Kenji Kimihara, 25	2:17.11
1967	David McKenzie, 24	2:15.45

TABLE IV-B

FIRST 50 FINISHERS IN BOSTON MARATHON 1967

1. Dave McKenzie, Greymouth, New Zealand, 2:15:45.
2. Tom Laris, New York A.C., 2:16:48.
3. Yutaka Aoki, Fukuoka, Japan, 2:17:17.
4. Louis C. Castagnola, Washington Sport Club, 2:17:48.
5. Antonio Ambu, Italy, 2:18:04.
6. Andrew Boychuk, Ontario, 2:18:17.
7. Takaski Inoue, Tokyo, Japan, 2:20:41.
8. Tooru Terasawa, Osaka, Japan, 2:21:17.
9. Dan McFadzean, Royal Navy, Cornwall, England, 2:22:06.
10. Kalevi Ihaksi, Finland, 2:22:07.
11. Eugene Comroe, So. Calif. Striders, 2:25:16.
12. John J. Kelley, BAA, 2:25:25.
13. Efren Carmona, Mexico, 2:25:59.
14. Mike Kimball, Santa Barbara A.C., 2:26:26.
15. Luis Buendia, Mexico, 2:27:23.
16. Steve Matthews, Denver Track Club, 2:27:52.
17. Ambrose Burfoot, Wesleyan Univ., 2:28:05.
18. Ron Daws, Twin Cities Track Club, 2:28:42.
19. Tom Osler, So. Jersey Track Club, 2:29:04.
20. Bill Harvey, New York City, 2:29:22.
21. Lt. Bill Clark, USMC, Camp LeJeune, N.C., 2:29:44.
22. Jim McDonagh, Millrose A.A., 2:29:55.
23. Orville Atkin, So. Calif. Striders, 2:30:26.
24. Jim Colpitts, Keesler AFB, Miss., 2:31:01.
25. Carl Weiser, Kegonsa T.C., 2:31:05.
26. Bill Schwab, New York A.C., 2:31:07.
27. Nick Kitt, Pasadena A.A., 2:31:56.
28. Jude Fuselier, New Orleans A.C., 2:32:05.
29. Philip Weiser, Twin Cities T.C., 2:32:18.
30. Gavin Jones, New York A.C., 2:32:20.
31. James Green, BAA, 2:33:15.
32. Guy Monnet, Mont Royal Francs-Amis, Quebec, 2:33:40.
33. John Brennand, Santa Barbara A.C., 2:33:58.
34. James Daley, No. Medford T.C., 2:34:12.
35. Len Lundmark, Twin Cities A.C., 2:34:20.
36. John Garlepp, Millrose A.C., 2:34:28.
37. John Duffield, Northwestern Univ., 2:34:45.
38. John Mowatt, Toronto Olympic Club, 2:34:59.
39. Ed Ayres, Central Jersey T.C., 2:35:10.
40. Bill Gordon, St. Anthony, B.C., 2:35:21.
41. Peter MacDonald, Hawaiian Road Runners Club, 2:35:39.
42. Richard Cordier, BAA, 2:35:40.
43. John Bair, Ohio Univ., 2:35:58.
44. Kenneth Mueller, BAA, 2:36:09.
45. Pablo Garrido, Mexico, 2:36:56.
46. Kenneth Shumate, Flint T.C., 2:37:12.
47. Dr. Gary Walton, Ohio T.C., 2:37:38.
48. Laurence Olson, Providence College A.A., 2:37:42.
49. Stephen Jackson, Peninsula T.C., Virginia, 2:37:44.
50. Albert Sewell, Ohio Valley T.C., 2:38:34.

The 50th in the Boston Marathon Race in 1967 clocked 2:38:34 hours. He would have been awarded the Olympic Gold Medal in 1896, 1900, 1904, and 1908 when the events were won in 2:58:50, 2:59:45, 3:28:53 and 2:55:18 respectively. In 1912, McArthur was victorious with a time of a 2:36:54; in 1920 Kolehmainen came first in 2:32:35. With these performances, they would not have been placed among the first 30 in the Boston race in 1967. In the same year, a 13-year-old girl finished the York University Marathon Race in Toronto, Canada, in 3:13:21.

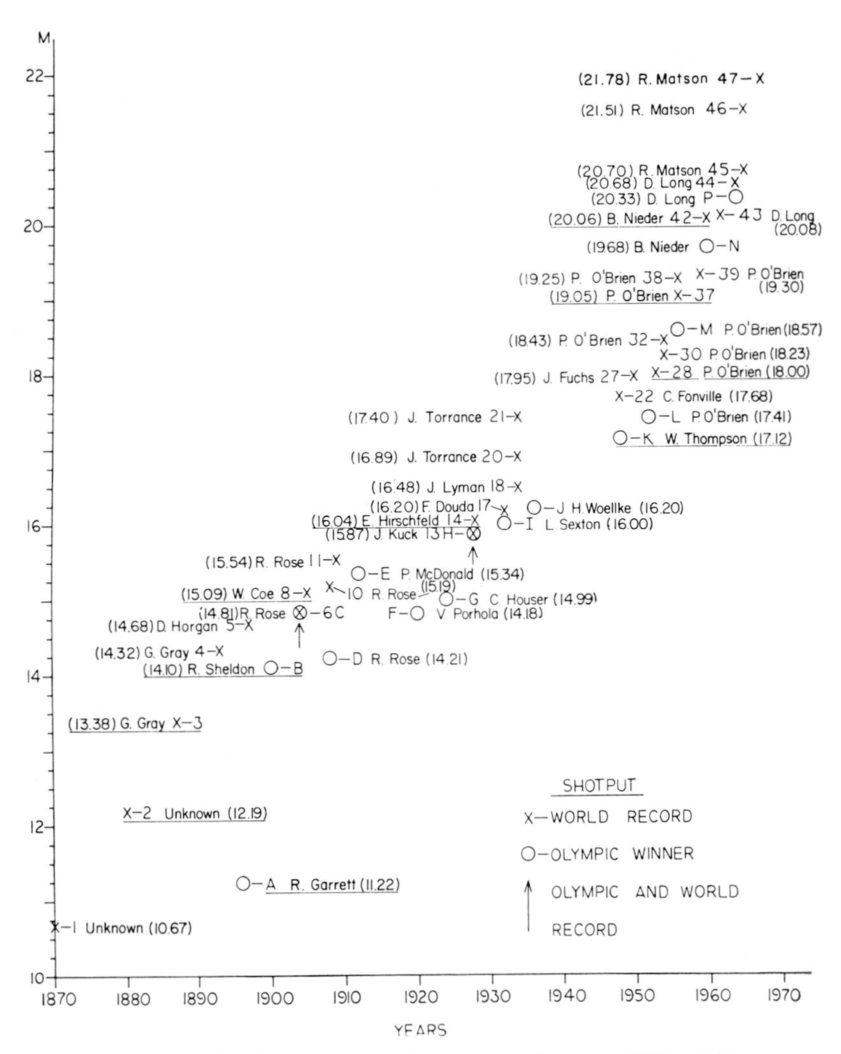

FIGURE 5. Development of world record in shot put (1870-1967).

TABLE V-A

COMPARISON OF "AVERAGE RECORDS"* FOR EACH SPORT OF THE PAST FOUR OLYMPIC GAMES

ATHLETICS AVERAGE OF WINNERS (MEN)

Events	*Helsinki*	*Melbourne*	*Rome*	*Tokyo*
100m	10″433	10″600	10″283	10″285
200m	20″966	20″966	20″716	20″615
400m	46″616	47″316	45″450	45″600
800m	1′49″800	1′48″400	1′47″933	1′46″016
1500m	3′45″766	3′42″133	3′39″150	3′39″550
5000m	14′13″700	13′57″066	13′47″366	† 13′49″600
10000m	29′42″666	29′07″766	28′40″950	28′36″566
110m Hurdles	14″250	14″116	14″100	† 13″800
400m Hurdles	52″433	52″000	50″050	50″233
3000m Steeplechase	8′52″566	8′43″733	8′46″766	8′35″000
High Jump	1. 985	2. 048	2. 120	2. 140
Long Jump	7. 333	7. 441	7. 940	† 7. 745
Triple Jump	15. 535	16.026	16. 453	16.473
Pole Vault	4. 391	4. 406	4. 566	5. 033
Shot Put	16. 896	17. 581	18. 511	19. 476
Discus Throw	52. 765	54. 070	56. 721	58. 898
Javelin Throw	71. 795	77. 838	79. 610	80. 230
Hammer Throw	57. 798	61. 966	65. 376	† 67. 996
4 × 100m Relay	40″600	40″183	* 40″140	39″316
4 × 400m Relay	3′07″316	* 3′07″320	3′05″266	3′02″650
Decathlon ‡	p. 6843. 500	p. 7257. 500	p. 7755. 500	p. 7770. 333
20km Walk	—	1°32′25″433	1°35′31″633	1°31′41″566
50km Walk	4°31′16″600	4°40′29″800	4°29′31″333	† 4°14′32″533
Marathon	2°25′47″566	2°27′40″500	2°17′57″966	2°16′20″213

*—Average of *best five* placed winners

†—Event took place during rain

‡—New method of scoring

AVERAGE OF BEST *Twelve* (MEN)*

Events	*Helsinki*	*Melbourne*	*Rome*	*Tokyo*
100m	10″525	10″491	10″333	10″308
200m	21″283	21″141	20″866	20″741
400m	46″766	46″891	45″941	46″025
800m	1′50″683	1′49″650	1′45″500	1′46″608
1500m	3′47″500	3′43″866	3′41″333	3′40″263
5000m	14′17″800	14′08″383	13′56″616	13′51″166
10000m	30′00″366	29′35″550	28′53″891	28′58″650
110m Hurdles	14″458	14″175	14″116	13″966
400m Hurdles	52″375	51″375	50″858	50″533
300m Steeplechase	8′57″166	8′47″200	8′46″650	8′36″716
High Jump	1. 946	2. 025	2. 075	2. 114
Long Jump	* 7. 133	7. 304	7. 712	7. 663
Triple Jump	15. 171	15. 778	16. 065	16. 291
Pole Vault	4. 270	4. 295	4. 483	4. 883
Shot Put	16. 170	16. 947	17. 896	18. 903
Discus Throw	50. 770	52. 375	55.120	57. 478
Javelin Throw	69. 545	73. 713	77. 500	76. 964
Hammer Throw	56. 090	60. 052	64. 243	66. 635
4 × 100m Relay	41″100	40″641	40″533	39″625
4 × 400m Relay	3′10″750	3′10″033	3′07″375	3′05″258
Decathlon ‡	p. 6425. 833	p. 6690. 333	p. 7333. 016	p. 7625. 500
20km Walk	—	1°34′04″050	1°37′11″250	1°32′35″083
50km Walk	4°37′30″116	4°53′42″783	4°34′35″983	4°18′19″433
Marathon	2°28′22″236	2°30′58″583	2°19′45″616	2°18′34″766

*—Average of *best eleven*

‡—New method of scoring

TABLE V-B

AVERAGE OF WINNERS (WOMEN)

Events	*Helsinki*	*Melbourne*	*Rome*	*Tokyo*
100m	11″866	11″766	11″350	11″000
200m	24″250	23″916	24″583	23″330
400m	—	—	—	53″630
800m	—	—	2′05″750	2′02″200
80m Hurdles	* 11″180	11″050	11″033	10″683
High Jump	1. 615	1. 685	1. 718	1. 773
Long Jump	5. 970	6. 021	6. 218	6. 461
Shot Put	14. 326	15. 788	16. 468	17. 346
Discus Throw	45. 790	50. 755	52. 373	56. 366
Javelin Throw	48. 198	50. 375	53. 208	56. 783
4 × 100m Relay	46″450	45″433	45″020	44″205
Pentathlon	—	—	—	p. 4926. 833

*—Average of *best five* placed winners

(AVERAGE OF BEST *Twelve* (WOMEN)*

Events	*Helsinki*	*Melbourne*	*Rome*	*Tokyo*
100m	11″908	11″700	11″683	11″476
200m	24″491	24″183	23″666	23″726
400m	—	—	—	53″866
800m	—	—	2′07″041	2′04″733
80m Hurdles	11″150	10″983	11″041	10″741
High Jump	1. 583	1. 658	1. 684	1. 740
Long Jump	5. 834	5. 885	6. 115	6. 372
Shot Put	13. 567	15. 024	15. 664	16. 629
Discus Throw	43. 246	47. 365	50. 485	54. 741
Javelin Throw	45. 345	48. 445	51. 482	54. 300
4 × 100m Relay	46″966	* 45″222	* 45″881	45″341
Pentathlon	—	—	—	p. 4774. 833

*—Average of *best nine*

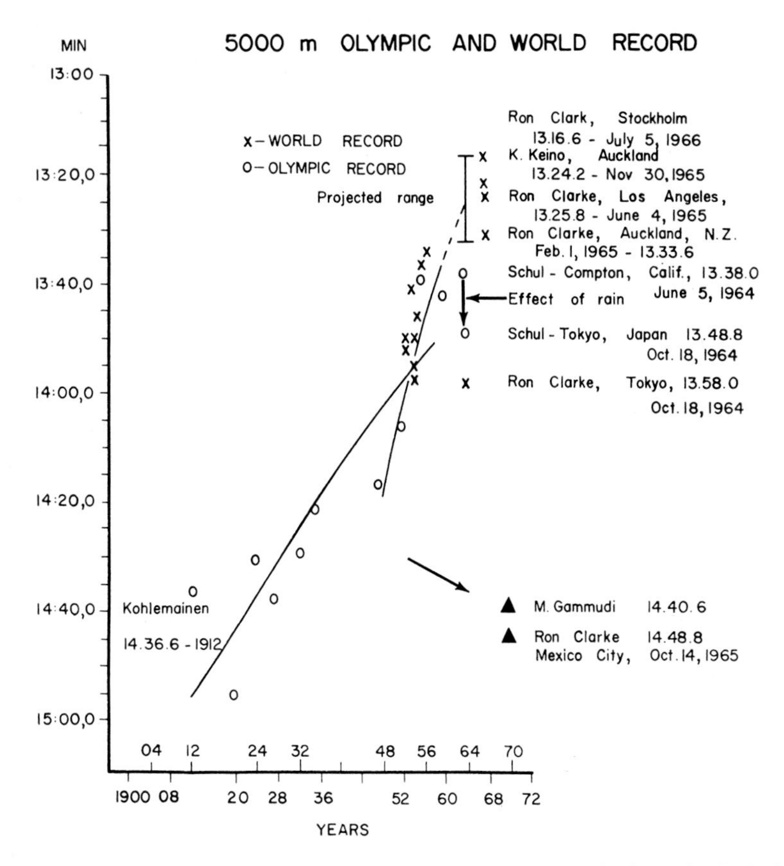

FIGURE 6. Growth curves for the 5,000-meter running record, since the inclusion of the event in the Olympic games program in 1912. Both world and Olympic performances were used for the statistical computations. The parabolic growth pattern during the period 1912-1936 seemed to be terminated by World War II (see Olympic winning performance in 1948). However, during the following years a remarkable performance improvement was in evidence (compare the steepness of the ascent of the post-1948 curve). Schul's winning performance in Tokyo of 13:48.8 was significantly slower than the projected performance level for 1964 (see dotted line and vertical range of standard deviation). The fact that the 5,000-meter final in Tokyo was run during torrential rain of course affected the time. But even Schul's best performance at Compton, California on June 5, 1964 of 13: 38 min was "substandard." That our extrapolation was valid can be seen by the subsequent improvement of the record, leading up to Keino's race of 13:24.2 min in November 1965 and Clarke's magnificent world record run of 13:16.6 in Stockholm on July 5, 1966. The dotted line

——————→

TABLE V-C

	Rope-Climbing Sec	Long Jump M	Throwing M	Sprinting Sec
1905-09		2.85		13.5
1913		3.06		12.9
1933		3.92		12.2
1943	6.4	4.14	33.13	11.6
1952	5.7	4.33	35.39	11.4
1957	5.4	4.42	35.39	11.3
1962	5.2	4.49	38.89	11.1

"Schweizer Turnprüfung"

Average performances in four standardized exercise tests conducted with Swiss recruits from 1905 to 1962.

TABLE V-D

On the Olympic qualifying list for 1968 the following events require better performances than those that would have won in the 1952 or 1956 Olympics.

100 meters — The qualifying time is 10.3 seconds. Bobby Morrow won the event in 1956 in 10.5.

800 meters — The qualifying time is 1:48. Mal Whitfield won in 1952 in 1:49.2.

1,500 meters — The qualifying time is 3:42. Joseph Barthel of Luxemberg won in 1956 at 3:45.2.

5,000 meters — The qualifying time is 13:50. Emil Zatopek of Czechoslovakia won in 1952 at 14:06.0.

10,000 meters — The qualifying time is 29 minutes. Zatopek won in 1952 with 29:17.0.

3,000 meters steeplechase — The qualifying time is 8:45. Horace Ashenfelter won in 1952 at 8:45.4.

Long jump — The qualifying distance is 25-1. Jerome Biffle won in 1952 with 24-10.03.

High jump — The qualifying height is 7-0. Charles Dumas won in 1956 at 6-11¼.

Shot Put —. The qualifying distance is 62 feet. Parry O'Brien won in 1956 at 60-11.

Discus — The qualifying distance is 190-3. Al Oerter won in 1956 at 184-11.

Hammer throw — The qualifying distance is 216-6½. Harold Connolly won in 1956 with a throw of 207-3½.

Pole vault — The qualifying height is 16-1. Don Bragg won in 1960 at 15-5⅛.

Javelin — The qualifying distance is 262 feet. Cy Young won in 1952 with 242-0.79.

---

was extrapolated in 1960. Though during the ensuing 4 years performances did not seem to corroborate the validity of the predictive computation, the conspicuous improvement of the world record during 1965 and 1966 speaks for itself. (Note the placement of the Clarke and Gammudi performances in Mexico City on October 14, 1965. On October 19, 1967, Gammudi won the 5,000 meter race at the 'Pre-Olympic Games' at Mexico City in almost exactly the same time: 14:41.0 min.)

Chapter II

PATTERNS OF EVOLUTION AND PREDICTABILITY OF ATHLETIC RECORDS

TRENDS OF DEVELOPMENT of athletic records during the past twenty years were sufficiently consistent to allow the fitting of "families of parabolas" for Olympic track and field and swimming events (Frucht *et al.*, 1964). Compared with the curves of growth of records covering the decades before World War II, these parabolas ascended more steeply. For the representation of growth of records in running and swimming parabolas of *fourth* degree, and in jumping and throwing of *second* degree gave the best fit.

World records usually precede improvements of Olympic records though the curves for both run parallel. Thus it was possible to construct aggregate parabolas from the combined data for world and Olympic records and so to reduce the influence of chance modifications.

Extrapolated and Measured Data

Extrapolated data invariably represent calculated abstractions that are free from chance influence. By contrast, all *individual* performances are subject to unpredictable modifications. In interpreting actual performances it is therefore necessary to evaluate them against the mathematically derived curves for the event under reference.

Coaches and athletes look upon the problem differently. They hold that significance attaches to measured performances only and that predictive computations based upon statistical analyses are of purely theoretical interest. They test the "correctness" of the latter by comparing them with the former. However, from the scientific point of view such an approach is invalid.

Each *extrapolated* datum derived from the growth curves or records represents a mean value, *viz.* the statistically most likely forecast for a given event, while according to the laws of probability, every *measured* performance may lie within a certain range above or below this mean value. It is improbable that it will coincide with the extrapolated datum although it occasionally comes very close to it. *The exact position of a single performance can never be predicted.* The empirical view that it is impossible to foretell precisely individual athletic performances is, therefore, correct.

Tables VI-VIII show estimated performances for Tokyo 1964. Their standard deviations were expressed as units of s, as well as in percentage. Of the thirty-three performance estimates, fourteen were for running, six for jumping, seven for throwing events, (eight of the track and field events for women) and six for swimming (three of them for women).

TABLE VI

TOKYO PERFORMANCES IN RUNNING EVENTS

Performances, Men and Women, (I) and Extrapolations (II) (means and anticipated ranges) as Published Prior to 1964 Olympic Games (with deviations of I from II, expressed as units of S and as percentage values).*

Tokyo 1964 M-Men W-Women	Event	I Measured Performance	II Extrapolated Performance (Mean)	Range	Deviation in Units of S	Percentage Deviation
M	10.000 m	28:24.4	28:10.89	28:01.38 28:20.29	—1.44	—0.80
M	5.000 m	13:48.8	13:23.37	13:15.29 13:31.08	--3.30	—3.17
M	1.500 m	3:38.1	3:32.01	3:31.35 3:32.67	—9.26	—2.87
M	800 m	1:45.1	1:45.67	1:45:09 1·46.12	+0.98	+0.48
M	400 m	0:45.1	0:45.08	0:44.22 0:45.78	—0.03	—0.04
M	100 m	0:10.0	0:10.07	0:09.90 0:10.23	—0.41	+0.70
M	100 m	0:11.4	0:10.95	0:10.83 0:11.07	—3.88	—4.11
M	4.400 m Relay	3:00.7	2:59.85	2:58.01 3:01.61	—0.48	—0.47
M	4.100 m Relay	0:39.0	0:38.91	0:38.74 0:39.07	—0.59	—0.24
M	4.100 m Relay	0:43.6	0:43.52	0:43.04 0:43.96	—0.19	—0.20
M	3.000 m St. Ch.	8:30.8	8:23.92	8:19.93 8:27.68	—1.83	—1.37
M	400 m Hurdles	0:49.6	0:48.74	0:43.54 0:48.93	—4.55	—1.76
M	110 m Hurdles	0:13.6	0:13.49	0:13.38 0:13.59	—1.10	—0.82
W	80 m Hurdles	0:10.5	0:10.52	0:10.39 0:10.64	+0.16	+0.19

*After Frucht and Jokl.

TABLE VII

TOKYO PERFORMANCES IN FIELD EVENTS

Performances of Men and Women, (I) and Extrapolations (II) (means and anticipated ranges) as Published Prior to 1964 Olympic Games (with deviations of I from II, expressed as units of S and as percentage values).*

Tokyo, 1964 M-Men W-Women	Event	Measured Performance	Extrapolated Performance (Mean)	Range	Deviation in Units of S	Percentage Deviation
M	Broad Jump	8.07	8.128	7.926 8.325	—0.29	—0.71
W	Broad Jump	6.76	6.568	6.379 6.753	+1.04	+2.92
M	Hop, Step and Jump	16.85	17.177	16.984 17.366	—1.69	—1.91
M	High Jump	2.18	2.228	2.217 2.238	—4.47	—2.15
W	High Jump	1.90	1.923	1.880 1.964	—0.54	—1.20
M	Pole Vault	5.10	4.822	4.757 4.885	+4.36	+5.77
M	Shot Put	20.33	20.063	19.706 20.413	+0.76	+1.33
W	Shot Put	18.14	18.417	18.206 18.624	—1.31	—1.50
M	Hammer Throw	69.74	70.691	70.222 41.150	—2.03	—1.35
M	Javelin	82.66	89.724	86.072 93.238	—1.93	—7.87
W	Javelin	60.54	58.986	58.164 59.703	+1.90	+2.63
M	Discus	61.00	59.953	59.250 60.647	+1.51	+1.75
W	Discus	57.27	56.187	52.590 59.568	+0.32	+1.93

*After Frucht and Jokl.

TABLE VIII

TOKYO PERFORMANCES IN SWIMMING

Performances of Men and Women, (I) and Extrapolations (II) (means and anticipated ranges) as Published Prior to 1964 Olympic Games (with deviations of I from II, expressed as units of S and as percentage values).*

Tokyo 1964 M-Men W-Women	Event	I Measured Performance	II Extrapolated Performance (Mean)	Range	Deviation in Units of S	Percentage Deviation
M	1.500 m Free Style	17:01.7	17:07.33	16:57.52 17:16:65	+0.57	+0.55
M	400 m Free Style	4:12.2	4:14.82	4:13.01 4:16.54	+1.45	+1.03
W	400 m Free Style	4:43.3	4:43.57	4:40.36 4:46.45	+0.09	+0.10
M	100 m Free Style	0:53.4	0:54.20	0:53.67 0:54.70	+1.51	+1.48
W	100 m Free Style	0:59.5	0:58.96	0:57.85 0:59.97	—0.53	—0.92
W	100 m Back Stroke	1:07.7	1:08.2	1:06.86 1:09.09	+0.28	+0.47

*After Frucht and Jokl.

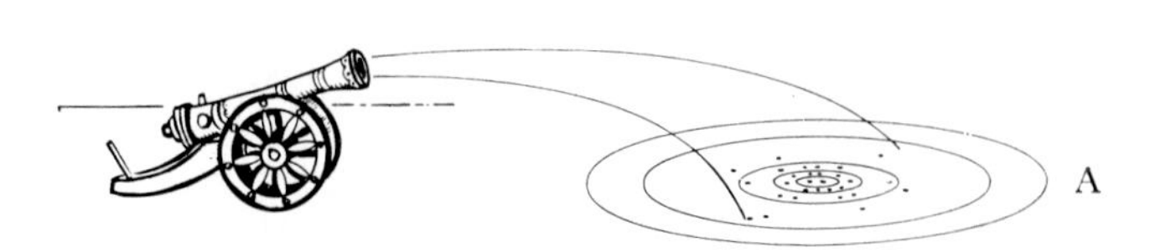
A

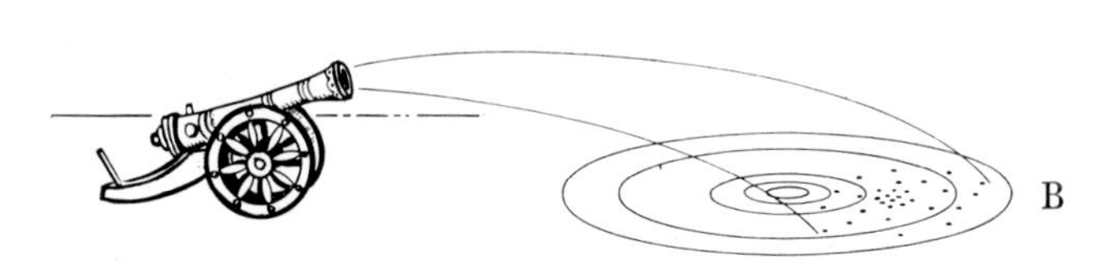
B

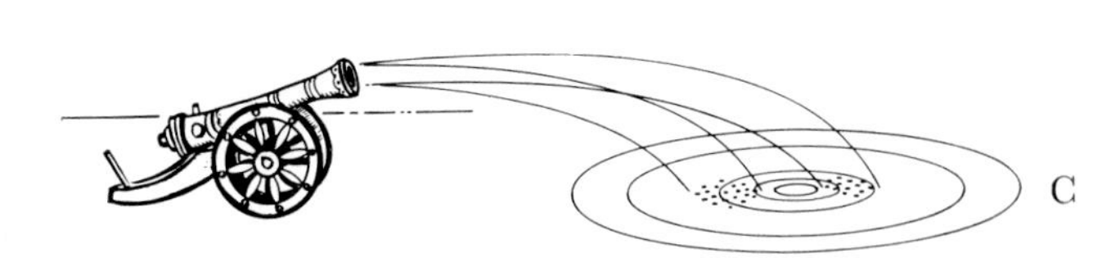
C

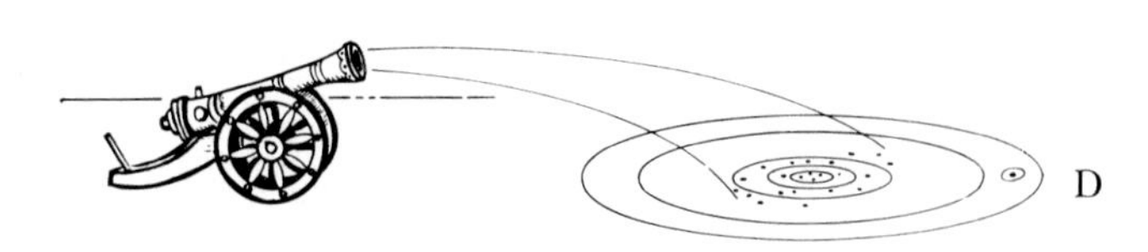
D

The data group themselves around the extrapolated reference points in accordance with a Gaussian distribution. About 95 percent of all measurements should therefore lie within ±1.96 s provided that only *chance* but no *systematic* disturbances had affected them.

Chance and Systematic Modifications

If one fires a cannon at a fixed aim, "chance influences" due to uncontrollable irregularities cause the hits to be scattered around the target (Fig .7). Even if the mean deviation were to amount to 0, distances between hits and target may be considerable, though the cannon's justation would thus be proved correct. On the other hand, negative or positive mean values of deviation would show the cannon's aiming mechanism to be in need of adjustment because of the occurrence of a "systematic disturbance" or of a "bias."

The mean deviation of the twenty-seven predictions of athletic events at Tokyo which were free of systematic influences was −0.0014; that is the actual performances differed from their predictions by as little as 0.14 percent (m.d. −0.11 s). This result is equivalent to a cannon missing its target at a distance of 10,000 yards by not more than fourteen yards.

FIGURE 7. "Chance" and "systematic" modification of physical performances: If one fires a cannon at a fixed aim, "chance influences" due to uncontrollable irregularities within the system cause the hits to be scattered around the target (*A*). Even if the mean deviation were to amount to 0, distances between hits and target may be considerable, though the cannon's justation would thus be proved correct. On the other hand, negative or positive mean values of deviation would show the cannon's aiming mechanism to be in need of adjustment because of the presence of a "systematic disturbance" or of a "bias" (*B*). A special kind of systematic disturbance exerting a bifocal effect is illustrated in (*C*) of which three examples are mentioned: altitude, noise and temperature. As regards altitude, conditions at Mexico City will facilitate running performances over short distances but represent a handicap in all endurance events. Similarly, noise made by spectators at games, rowing, swimming events and track and field meetings, is likely to stimulate the contestants, while absolute silence is a prerequisite for top class performances in equestrian dressage, golf, target shooting, and others. Thirdly, optimal temperatures for sprinting and long distance track races differ by 12° to 16° C, with high temperatures aiding the former and retarding the latter. The dot surrounded by a circle (*D*) represents world records falling outside the standard deviation belt above the growth curve of world records in which the majority of measurements lie.

The Tokyo results in their entirety divide themselves into two groups. One lies within an area of about two standard deviations from their predicted means, i.e. values whose differences from the predicted levels can have been due solely to chance influences (group 1). The other, which spreads beyond the range of two standard deviations (group 2) reflects systematic influences whose categorical nature is emphasized by the fact that it is separated from the group (1) by "unoccupied" belts extending from -2.03 s to -3.3 s, and from $+1.90$ s to $+4.36$ s, respectively (Fig. 4).

So far our cannon has been assumed to fire standard ammunition. Positive or negative deviations of hits reflecting systematic disturbances will in such a case be due to extraneous influences such as a steady following or a steady opposing wind. They could not be due to different properties of individual missiles.

The susceptibility of the various athletic disciplines towards *disturbances* is not constant. For example, results in jumping and throwing competitions are invariably less uniform than those of middle, long distance, relay and swimming races. The jumps and throws at Tokyo were distributed evenly over the entire range of ± two standard deviations, while *running and swimming* times were clustered within a much narrower belt of between $+1.03$ and -0.47 percent. The reasons for this difference in reproducibility of performances are *physiological* as well as *physical.* The long jump exemplifies the first. Here, a compromise has to be found between two inherently incommensurable adaptive requirements. While sprinting at maximal speed the athlete must place the tip of his foot exactly behind the outermost margin of the take-off board. The "computing capacities" of his nervous system are thus challenged to their limit.

As regards the second modality of disturbances, *viz.* those due to physical factors, reference is made to the javelin and discus throw. In these events constancy of maximal performances is unattainable because of the unpredictability of aerodynamic influences. The latter increase with the distance of the throws. In the discus throw for *women,* another physical factor has to be considered: The women's discus was developed by an arbitrary reduction of size and weight of the men's discus. The resultant ratio between mass and surface renders the women's discus conspicuously unstable. Nevertheless, although fluctuations of *individual* performances are therefore greater in women's than in men's contests, the respective *mean* values do not differ. Plus and minus deviations cancel each other out. This finding represents corroborating proof for the validity of the statistical method applied in this study.

Ranges of scatter greater than ± 2 s are commonly encountered in routine analyses of biophysical and biological random samples. The conclusion is therefore justified that the elaboration of *statistical* methods for the prediction of athletic performances more effective than those used in our Tokyo study is unlikely. On the other hand the precision of predicted data is likely to be further improved as a result of advancements of athletic techniques, of standardization of facilities, better equipment and enhanced environmental conditions, e.g. as a result of the introduction of indoor stadia like the recently built Astrodome in Houston, Texas.

World Records

A. H. Frucht has pointed out that world records represent unique physiological events for which there are no precedents in medical research. This is the reason why the sample from which our statistical computations were made is highly selective. The establishment of a world record invariably presupposes the presence of a combination of optimal conditions. That such conditions will be present during an Olympic final is possible, though not likely. A case in point was the 1964 Olympic swimming tournament which was held in a perfectly constructed indoor pool, while the 1960 swimming contests in Rome were still held in an open basin. Thus, a variety of extraneous sources of interference with maximal performances were eliminated during the Tokyo contests. By contrast, the track and field events at Tokyo were staged under distinctly less favorable conditions. The track was conspicuously slow. Several competitions took place during heavy rain or excessive heat or bitter cold. Thus, it was not surprising that in none of the single track and field events for men was a new world record established, while the results of the swimming tournament were outstanding. The data in Tables VI-VIII reflect "chance" modifications as they affected the swimming and track and field performances, individually as well as in their entirety. Also, sequelae of "systematic" modifications are in evidence, e.g. of the worldwide adoption during the preceding four years of the fiberglass pole which rendered obsolete the performance data from which the growth pattern of the world record in pole vaulting since 1900 had been computed until about 1962.

Environmental Modifications

A number of modifiers of athletic performances that had not previously been known were identified during the past two years. At the International Seminar on "Sport at Medium Altitude," held under the auspices of the International Council of Sport and Physical Education in December 1965 in Magglingen, Switzerland, E. R. Dickinson *et al.* of the Ballistic Research Laboratories of the United States Army Research and Development Group presented data showing that the altered air resistance coefficient at 2400 meters above sea level causes significant performance increases in the shot put, the hammer, discus and javeline throw, and that at the 1968 Olympic Games in Mexico City, improvements in these three events of magnitudes of the order of 5.8 cm, 53 cm, 69 cm and 162 cm, respectively may be expected (Fig. 8).

Another example of a previously unknown modifier of athletic efficiency is the discovery that hydrodynamic flow and drag patterns such as are invariably engendered along marginal contact surfaces between human body and swimming suit cause a decelerating effect upon velocity of progression in the water.* In January 1967, Miss Sylvia Ester of the German Democratic Republic established a new world record for 100-meter free style, swimming the distance naked.

*In 1949, Prof. A. V. Hill (*Science Today, 6*:341, 1949; *Nature, 164*:820, 1949; *Brit Med J,* Nov. 19, 1949, p. 1162.) dealt with the problem of "Design and Physical Performance." He analyzed the respective morphological and functional efficiency characteristics of the blue whale, the largest of the Cetacea, and the dolphin. The range of length between the two is 21 to 1, of weight 1000 to 1. In general shape there is a close correspondence. Both animals move in the water with unusual efficiency, cruising for long periods at 15 knots, being capable of short bursts of 20 knots or over. On the basis of weight of muscle the whale, Hill wrote, should have the easier task. However, if one examines the scale relationship between dolphins and whales in terms of the circulation of the blood, it becomes apparent that for reasons not now to be detailed it is impossible for the whale to generate horsepower in proportion to its weight. This accepted, Hill continued, "it follows that whales as well as dolphins possess a great capacity for inducting a smooth flow of water past their bodies, and that

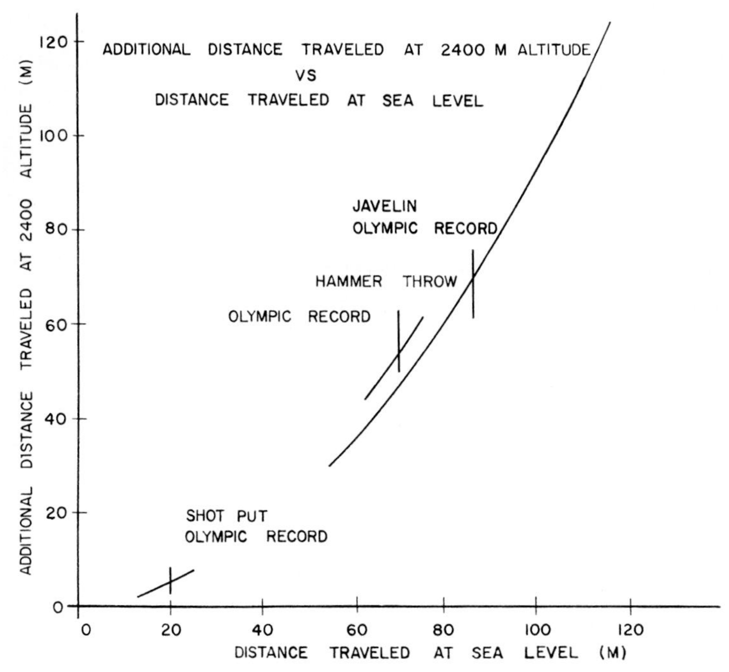

FIGURE 8. Effect of altitude at Mexico City (2,400 meters) upon distance traveled by standard shot put, hammer throw and javelin. (Courtesy E. R. Dickinson, M. J. Piddington and T. Brain.)

---

the performance of both should make ship designers envious." In his Royal Institution Christmas Lecture 1951 on "How Animals Move" (Cambridge, 1953) Professor James Gray writes as follows:

"If I were asked to name Nature's best swimmer I should undoubtedly choose the dolphin. The dolphin can maintain a speed of 20-25 m.p.h., and although we do not know precisely how long this speed can be kept up, the dolphin certainly does not tire anything like so quickly as a fish. Dolphins are mammals; they are warm-blooded and they breathe with lungs as we do. These advantages enable the animal to renew its muscular energy much faster than a cold-blooded fish can. Still, even allowing for these improvements in design, the dolphin is a very remarkable animal: If the resistance encountered by a dolphin gliding through water is the same as that of a rigid model of the same shape and size, the muscles that move its tail up and down must be about ten times more efficient than those of a dog or man. Alternatively, if the power of the muscles of a dolphin is the same as that of the same weight of muscle in other mammals, then the water must flow over the dolphin's body with ten times less disturbance than over a rigid model. If this is so, Nature's design for a dolphin is much more efficient than any submarine or torpedo yet produced by man."

Her time of 57.9 improved by a full second the previous record held by Miss Dawn Fraser of Australia.

The mode of the mechanical impact that is engendered if the human body progresses at high velocity through the air may determine performance limits in ski jumping. Table IX shows the growth of

TABLE IX

DEVELOPMENTS OF WORLD RECORD IN SKI JUMP

1879—1966

23 m	Hammesweit	Norway	1879
23 m	Lillehagen	Norway	1888
35.5 m	Tandberg	Norway	1900
41 m	Gjestvang	Norway	1902
48 m	Smith	Norway	1909
54 m	Amundsen	Norway	1914
58 m	Omstvedt	Norway	1916
61.5 m	A. Haugen	Norway	1917
63 m	Carlsen	Norway	1926
66 m	Snersund	Norway	1926
70 m	Thams	Norway	1926
70.5 m	S. Ruud	Norway	1926
72 m	S. Ruud	Norway	1927
72 m	Trojani	Switzerland	1928
75 m	Badrutt	Switzerland	1929
76.5 m	B. Ruud	Norway	1931
81.5 m	S. Ruud	Norway	1931
84 m	S. Ruud	Norway	1933
86 m	S. Ruud	Norway	1933
87 m	Ruchet	Switzerland	1933
87.5 m	Lymbourne	Canada	1933
92 m	B. Ruud	Norway	1934
93 m	R. Andersen	Norway	1935
95 m	Sorensen	Norway	1935
95 m	Maruszarz	Poland	1935
98 m	R. Andersen	Norway	1935
99 m	R. Andersen	Norway	1935
99 m	Kainersdorfer	Switzerland	1935
101 m	Bradl	Austria	1936
107 m	Bradl	Austria	1938
108 m	Gehring	Germany	1941
109 m	Mair	Germany	1941
112 m	Lahr	Germany	1941
112 m	Kraus	Germany	1941
118 m	Gehring	Germany	1941
120 m	Tschannen	Switzerland	1948
124 m	Gantschnigg	Switzerland	1950
133 m	Weiler	West Germany	1950
135 m	Netzell	Sweden	1950
139 m	Luiro	Finland	1951
141 m	Slibar	Yugoslavia	1961
141 m	Lesser	East Germany	1962
141 m	Sjoberg	Sweden	1964
142 m	Motejlek	Czechoslovakia	1964
144 m	Zandanel	Italy	1964
145 m	Lesser	East Germany	1965
145.5m	Wirkola	Norway	1966
146 m	Wirkola	Norway	1966

the record since 1879. The remarkable improvements are due to the overall improvement of physical efficiency that has occurred during the period under study, the construction of higher and better designed "Schanzen," as well as to the elaboration of aerodynamically superior techniques of takeoff and of flight (Figs. 9 and 10).

FIGURES 9 AND 10. Between 1893 and 1967 the record in the ski jump has grown from 15 to 150 meters. Uniform, equipment, style and variety of other determinants of performance have been identified and brought under control in scientific studies of the physiology of athletic records.

Women's Records

The status of women in Western society has greatly changed in the past few decades. In his *Psychological Studies of the Biography of Genius*, Professor Lewis M. Terman of Stanford University reported as late as 1940 that highly gifted women had little chance to develop their abilities. This is what he said:

> Although among my subjects with I.Q. scores of 140 and above the women equal or excel the men in school achievements from the first grade through college, after school days are over the great majority cease to compete with men in the world's work. If they do not marry at once they accept whatever kind of respectable employment is at hand. After marriage they fall into the domestic role and only in exceptional cases seek other outlets for their talents. The woman who is a

FIGURE 11A. The Kentucky Physical Fitness Experiment was designed to assess the physical and mental effects of a daily intensive training program upon 14-year-old high school boys and girls. Weight lifting was included in the exercise curriculum. Boys as well as girls responded to the sustained activity schedule with a significant increase in lean body tissue, pari passu with a loss of surplus fat.

> potential poet, novelist, lawyer, physician, or scientist usually gives up any professional ambition she may have had and devotes herself to home, husband and children. The exclusive devotion of women to domestic pursuits robs the arts and sciences of a large fraction of the genius that might otherwise be dedicated to them. My data strongly suggest that this loss must be debited to motivational causes and to limitations of opportunity rather than to lack of ability.*

A like statement would no longer be appropriate in 1967. The rate of development of women's athletic records during the past three decades has been more rapid than that of men. In part this phenomenon reflects a new attitude of society and thus is indicative of a steadily progressing liberation from taboos which had held the "second sex" back for millennia. Athletic training for girls today includes conditioning and preparatory practices which until not so many years ago simply "were not done" by "young ladies." For

FIGURE 11B. Tug-of-war demands maximal use of muscular power.

Science, 92:2388, Oct. 4, 1940.

example, it is only recently that weight training was introduced as part of the school physical exercise program for girls, and of their preparation for competitive sports. Nancy Green, the Canadian skiing champion who at age twenty-three weighed 125 lbs was able to do forty deep knee bends with a 170 lb barbell across her shoulders. One wonders what Victorian matrons would have said had they been confronted with the sight of young women practicing weight lifting in a gymnasium (Figs. 11A-C).

The extent to which every physiological component of girls' physical performance capacity — i.e. power, skill and endurance — has changed is apparent from the growth of records in all athletic disci-

FIGURE 11C. Every modern school physical training program must include activities which are capable of increasing muscular power. The above exercise represents examples of training suitable for the purpose.

plines. The best woman hurdlers today run the 80-meter distance 1.2 sec faster than in 1936; while the running speed of the leading female middle distance runners is currently approaching that of male four minute milers (Figs. 12 and 13). In 1967, sixteen women participated and completed the course of the 100 kilometer run organized annually at the Biel, Switzerland. Among the 1162 *male* contestants who entered the event, only 749 arrived at the finish. However, none of the *female* starters gave up. They all qualified for the silver medal award given to those who covered the distance in less than twenty-four hours.

FIGURE 12. Miss Packer winning the 800-meter race in Tokyo in 1964 in 2.01.1. min. Considering the great interest in the conquest by men of the 4 min "barrier," it is appropriate to point to the fact that the world record in the half-mile race for women is now approaching 2 min. Thus, the running speed in the middle distance for girls approximates that of the best male mile runners.

FIGURE 13. Finish of 80-meter hurdles race in Tokyo in 1964. Winner: Miss Karin Baltzer of the German Democratic Republic (third from right). Her time of 10.5 sec is 2 sec better than the world record of 1928. The fact that the entire field is close shows the overall improvement of this event which demands a unique combination of speed, skill and endurance.

Chapter III

GROWTH AND ATHLETIC PERFORMANCE

ERLING ASMUSSEN (1964) of Copenhagen has analyzed the effect of the acceleration of growth during the past decades upon athletic performances. He pointed out that not only do bodily dimensions like height and weight show a steady increase at all ages from birth to adulthood, but that also all physiological functions connected with sexual maturation are accelerated. For example, the age of menarche has shifted from seventeen years in 1840 to thirteen at present, and the adolescent spurt of growth, due to hormonal changes that characterize puberty, occurred in 1800 as late as seventeen in Norwegian boys, whereas now it begins at thirteen. Among the causes of this acceleration, Asmussen mentions better nutrition, more contact between isolated groups, less inbreeding, industrialization and urbanization, increasing world temperature, and better physical education. To these must be added the improved methods of control and prevention of the infectious diseases.

Though today's athletes are taller and heavier than in the twenties, their physiques have not changed qualitatively and geometrically. But the proportion between the cross-sectional areas of any muscle and its length has grown at a rate of 1.13:1. Athletes who are now 6 percent taller than those of 1927 possess 13 percent more muscular strength. The maximum work which the muscles of a typical decathlon competitor can yield today—computed as force and distance they can shorten—is 20 percent higher than thirty years ago.

Similar quantitative considerations apply to the effect upon performances of *endurance* of the size of the lungs, the size of the heart and the amount of hemoglobin in the blood, as well as to surface areas of alveoli, of walls of capillaries and of cross-sectional areas of aorta, coronary arteries, iliac arteries, and possibly the arterial system in its entirety. On account of the general increase in body length and body mass alone, today's athletes must be capable of attaining maximum oxygen uptake levels that are 13 percent higher. However, athletes who excel in exercises such as long distance running, cycling, swimming and skiing are distinguished by specific morphological and functional characteristics of their cardiorespiratory systems; that is they are not, or at least not necessarily, taller and heavier than their predecessors were prior to World Wars I and II, but they have proportionately larger hearts, larger aortae, larger coronary arteries and larger lungs. The greatest performance increase during the past half century has occurred in branches of athletics which require *strength;* most athletic performances requiring *endurance* have increased at a lesser rate. The available empirical data are not yet fully understood. For example, percentage-wise the world record in 1500-meter *swimming* has improved four times as much as the world record in 5000-meter *running.* Both events are of comparable duration. There is also the fact mentioned before that the increment in physical performances of *women* has been much greater in swimming than in running and jumping.

Since both boys and girls now reach maturity faster, their physical performances approach adult values at an earlier age. Asmussen and Heeboll-Nielsen (1961) as well as Ikai (1964) have demonstrated that the increase in muscular strength in boys during puberty is out of proportion to their increase in body dimensions. Jokl showed that this increase of strength during puberty is paralleled by an increase in endurance and therefore presumably also of aerobic capacity. This statement, however, applies only to *boys.* In *girls* the increase in strength during puberty is accompanied by a decrease in physical endurance (Fig. 20). The issue is complicated by the fact that the studies under reference were conducted with untrained boys and girls. Sustained training engenders modifications the magnitude of which differs for various performance sectors. For example, the observation of the extraordinary large aerobic capacity of young girl swimmers does not allow general conclusions to be drawn in respect of the physical endurance of young girls in other sports. In 1967, a fourteen-year-old American girl swimmer, Debbie Meyer, established a world record for the 1500-meter swimming distance with a performance of 17 minutes 50.2 seconds, which surpasses the time attained by the winner in the same event for *men* at the 1956 Olympic Games in

Melbourne. But *no correspondingly outstanding performances of endurance by young girls have so far occurred in long distance running, skiing, or cycling.*

Asmussen (1964) mentions that in *gymnastics* the load on the body's muscles is the weight of the body itself. In "chinning," a tall man's stronger arm muscles must lift his heavier body and no advantage will therefore accrue in this kind of exercise from being tall. For mechanical reasons the combination of muscular strength and a *short* body represents in fact a most favorable prerequisite for success in gymnastics as the outstanding performances by the Japanese at the Olympic Games have demonstrated.

Acceleration of Growth

In most parts of the world a threefold change in human development is currently taking place: an acceleration of growth, a deceleration of aging, and a lengthening of the span of life. Children develop quicker and mature earlier than in the past. Adults age more slowly. An average sized British high school student does not fit into the armor of medieval knights in the Tower of London (Fig. 14). The beautiful eighteenth century wedding dresses on display in the National Museum in Helsinki are too small for today's brides in Finland. Between 1900 and 1950 life expectancy in the United States increased from under fifty to over seventy years. In considering the impact of these developmental trends upon athletics, attention must be paid also to the effectiveness of selection of young men and women with known aptitudes for certain sports, for example of tall persons for basketball, or of bulky and muscular individuals for the shot put, the discus and the hammer throw (Fig. 15).

The acceleration of growth has led to increasingly larger numbers of young as well as of older men and women competing in international sporting events. Sonja Henie became queen of the skating rink at the age of thirteen. Bob Mathias won the Olympic decathlon in 1948 at seventeen. Many high school track and field records today are much better than the official world records were twenty years ago. The best U.S. girl swimmers in Tokyo in 1964 were between fourteen and eighteen years of age. A seventeen-year-old Romanian high school girl, Mihaela Penes, who won the javelin contest in Tokyo

FIGURE 14. Seventeen-year-old average sized American high school boy standing next to knight's armor made in 15th century. The latter may be assumed to have been worn by members of a population group whose physiques were superior to those of the majority of their contemporaries. The picture reflects the magnitude of the effect of the acceleration of growth in the past centuries.

with a throw of 60.54 meters was the youngest woman ever to gain an Olympic gold medal in a track and field event. In 1965, a fifteen-year-old Russian girl, Larissa Petrik, won a gymnastic competition against the twenty-seven-year-old Olympic champion of 1964, Larissa Latinyna. Several other girls of between twelve and fifteen have recently come to the fore in gymnastics. At the gymnastic world championships held in Dortmund, Germany, in 1966, Natalia Kutchinskaja, the sixteen-year-old Soviet schoolgirl, won the competitions on the parallel bars, the horse and the free exercises. A fourteen-year-old girl, Crista Laprell of Bavaria, was one of Germany's best slalom skiers in 1965. Several European countries have started special schools to provide gifted children with opportunities to develop their athletic capacities during their junior years. At age eighteen, Betty Cuthbert

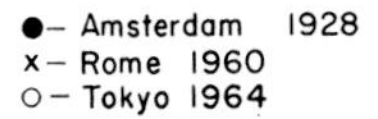

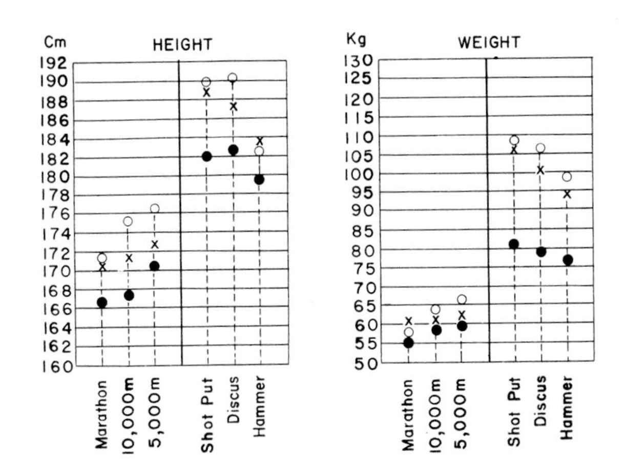

FIGURE 15. Height and weight measurements of finalists in the throwing events and in the long distance races at the Olympic Games in Amsterdam in 1928, Rome in 1960, and in Tokyo in 1964. The diagram shows that the two groups under reference differ in respect to their "somatotypes," as well as the fact that acceleration of growth and increased emphasis upon selection of athletes with special aptitude for various competitions have exerted their influence during the period under reference.

The situation is similar in respect to increments of maximal oxygen intake levels. In 1937, Robinson, Edwards and Dill wrote about laboratory studies with five leading track athletes, "all of them in good running form at the time of experiments." The first of these was Lash, who within the preceding year had established a new world record in the two-mile run; the second was Cunningham who held world records in the mile run; the third and fourth, San Romani and Venzke, were milers on the U.S. Olympic team; the fifth, Fenske, had run the mile in near record time. The authors considered one of the most remarkable observations in their experiment Lash's consumption of over 5 liters of oxygen per min. (The highest intake figure obtained by Lash in a run on a treadmill at 21.6 kph with no grade was 5.35 liters per min.). These figures far exceeded previous records of a similar character, such as those obtained by Henderson and Haggard (1925) with Yale oarsmen; by Christensen (1931) with Danish cyclists; and by Hill (1927) with Cornell runners.

In 1956 P. O. Astrand reported maximal oxygen intake levels of 5.38, 5.49 and 5.88 liters per min, respectively, in three Swedish Olympic skiing champions, P. E. Larsson, L. Larsson and S. Jernberg.

In 1965 H. Mellerowicz and G. Hansen communicated maximal intake levels of 5.8, 6.0, 5.9 and 5.9, respectively, in the members of the German rowing crew of Australia won three Olympic gold medals (100 meter, 200 meter and relay) in 1956. She added a fourth Olympic victory eight years later when she came in first in the 400-meter final at the Tokyo Games in 1964 (Fig. 16).

Following the sucessful American tour in 1963 of the well known German rowing "Achter" crew of Ratzeburg during which they beat Georgetown University, Princeton, Columbia, Cornell and Philadelphia, thus proving themselves the world's best eight for the year, their coach Karl Adam pointed out that his men had started to train for competition at age fifteen while American rowers began with their boat practice not before age seventeen or eighteen:

FIGURE 16. Miss Cuthbert (fourth runner from left) at last baton change-over in the 4 × 100-meter relay final in Melbourne, 1956, in which her team came in first. Eight years later, Miss Cuthbert won the 400-meter race at the Tokyo Olympic games.

---

of the Four with Cox (Neusel, Britting, Werner and Hirschfelder), that won the Olympic Games in Tokyo in 1964.

The magnitude of increments during the past four decades of the physiological capacities upon which range and limitations of oxygen intake during exhausting exercise depend is comparable to those of the anthropometric measurements of Olympic finalists in the throwing events.

The improvements of Olympic and world records in both kinds of athletic events, *viz.* those reflecting power and endurance, during the years under analysis, have followed corresponding trends of their morphological and functional prerequisites.

> This difference alone would suffice to explain the superiority of my crew. In order to attain international performance standards in rowing, intensive conditioning and rowing training must begin not later than age 15.

In the intervening four years the principal of starting specialized training for competitive sports of all kinds at age fifteen or earlier has been universally adopted, especially in swimming, ice skating and gymnastics. In the German Democratic Republic where the scientific study of athletics receives exemplary support, special schools for gifted children provide promising young boys and girls with opportunities to develop their physical potentialities pari passu with their intellectual education.

However, it is remarkable that no man under twenty-one won a gold medal in the track and field contests in Tokyo in 1964. The winners of the marathon, the 3000-meter steeple chase, the 20- and 50-km walking competitions and the hammer throw were over thirty. The winner in the women's javelin was seventeen, in the discus and shot-put twenty-seven. The youngest male Olympic champion in gymnastics was twenty-three, the oldest thirty-two. The corresponding age range for women gymnasts was twenty-two to twenty-nine. The best swimmers were younger. The youngest gold medallist among the male swimmers was seventeen, the oldest twenty-two (with a twenty-five-year-old winning the high diving). Two women swimming champions were fifteen, and the four oldest seventeen! Only the springboard diving victory went to a "matron" of twenty-one. Three Olympic gold medals were won by men of over forty—in yachting (star class), the Grand Prix Equestrian Jumping and the Grand Prix Equestrian Dressage.

Girl Swimmers

Astrand, Engstrom, Eriksson, Karlberg, Nylander, Saltin and Thoren (1963) of Stockholm have evaluated physical and mental development, social and family background, physiological performance capacity and medical status of thirty of the best Swedish girl swimmers, ages twelve to sixteen. Among them, the girls held two world records, three European records and four Swedish championships. The mean age at which they had learned to swim was 5.8 years, ranging from 2.5 to eight years. The duration of their active training varied from one to four years. Thirteen had swum for two years or less, none for more than four years.

The girls were drawn from four leading clubs, referred to as A, B, C and D. Those belonging to club D practiced for three to four hours per week and covered a total distance of between four and seven kilometers; those belonging to club B—with one exception—for about twenty-eight hours covering between fifty-eight and sixty-eight kilometers (Fig. 17). The differences in "training volume" influenced the girls' performances in a decisive manner. When proficiency levels in their competitions were assessed according to an international point scale, a mean value of 510 was obtained for the girls of club D as against one of 876 for club B.

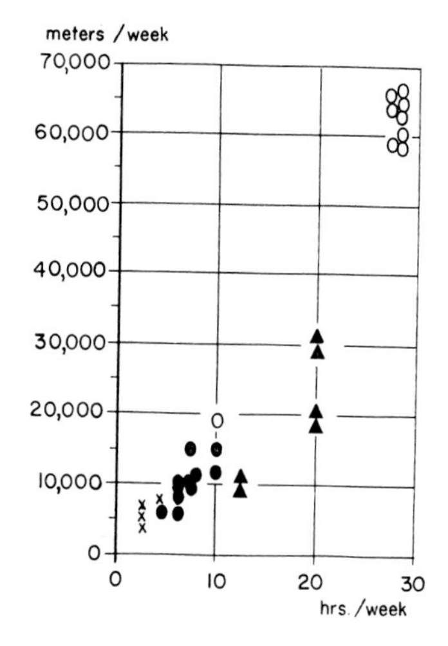

FIGURE 17. The training expressed as the number of swimming hours and meters per weeks provides a measure of the intensity, and has been denoted collectively as the *training volume.* Club A •; club B o; club C ▲; club D x. Their swimming proficiency is expressed by

Club	No.	Points	
		Mean	Range
A	11	627	428-780
B	9	876	620-1104
C	6	647	325-931
D	4	510	365-595

(Courtesy P.– O. Astrand *et al.,* 1963.)

Most of the girls came from homes which were socially and economically better situated than those of a control group of nonathletic children. The method of upbringing of the thirty girls was described as somewhat "old-fashioned and authoritarian," their home situation as very happy. In twenty-eight of the thirty girls' families, one or both parents had taken part in sports competitions and belonged to the same swimming club as their children whom they had introduced as members at an early age. The attitude of the parents as to their children's participation in swimming contests was distinctly favorable and they cooperated well with the coaches. Twenty-nine of the girls' thirty-eight brothers and sisters were also active in athletics. The mothers said that swimming had solved the question of their daughters' leisuretime activities in a healthy way.

The medical examination indicated that the lengthy daily swimming lessons had in no way exerted an unfavorable influence. More especially, the risk of respiratory or other infections was not increased.

As a group the girls were taller than average. A review of school growth records showed that even at age seven their height had been taller than average. Evidently, the accelerated development noted after age twelve had not been caused by the intensive training. Body weight in relation to body height was normal. In most of the girls, adolescence had occurred early. All of them stated that they competed if a swimming event occurred during their menstrual period.

The psychologist reported that the girls were "frank, extroverted, energetic and active." Their friends and parents described them as "always on the go." Only in six cases had the time-consuming swimming practice interfered with their homework. The girls looked upon the daily training, the association with other club members and the traveling in connection with their competitions as most pleasurable. Many had additional interests or hobbies: Eight played a musical instrument; five took part in other sports such as basketball, competitive gymnastics, tennis and horse riding. Several did country dancing. A strikingly large number already had purposeful plans for future careers.

Emotionally, the girls seemed mature for their age. Intellectually they were normally developed. Twenty-one of them had distinctly superior intelligence. The school grades of eighteen were above average; two were average; and only ten were slightly below average. None of them smoked or took "strong drinks." They were all well adjusted. The intense training had not harmed them in any way; on the contrary, it appeared to have contributed to the favorable personality development which the study revealed.

The physiological investigation indicated significantly superior functional dimensions. The most striking findings were the large sizes of the girls' hearts (Fig. 18), and an enhanced capacity to take up oxygen during work (Fig. 19). Lung volumes were above normal averages by 11 to 15 percent, total hemoglobin by 19 percent, blood volume by 14 percent, heart volume by 22 percent, and maximal oxygen intakes by 10 percent. These results were demonstrably related to the girls' outstanding athletic performances. By contrast, pulse rates at rest did not differ from those of untrained children. Since many adult athletes have resting pulse rates of 50 and below, the above finding suggests that this physiological feature does not play an essential part in the integrative build-up of superb physical performances of endurance.

Such differences in functional and performance capacity as were

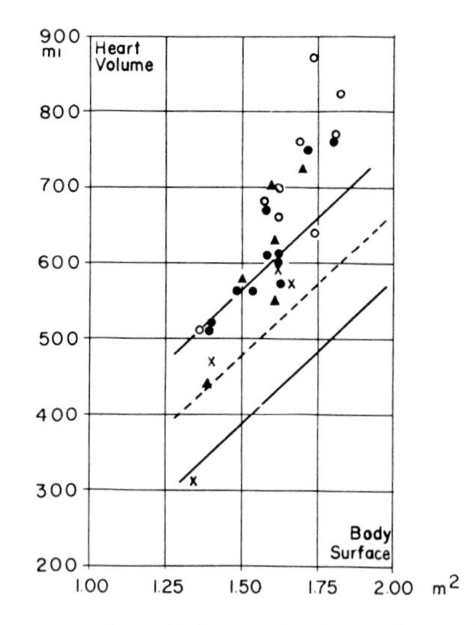

FIGURE 18. Heart volume in relation to body surface. *Broken line:* normal regression with 95 percent confidence interval. (Courtesy P.–O. Astrand *et al.*, 1963.)

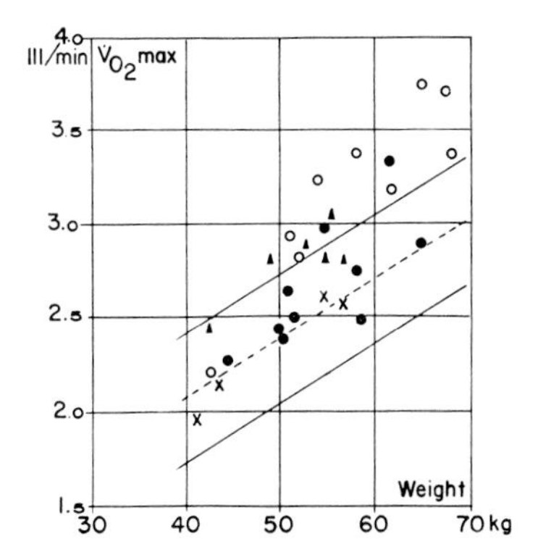

FIGURE 19. Oxygen uptake during maximal work on the bicycle ergometer in relation to body weight. *Broken line:* normal regression line with 95 percent confidence interval. Regression equation: $y = 0.81 + 0.032\ x$; $r = 0.86$; S. D. $= \pm\ 0.34$; $n = 42$. Courtesy P.–O. Astrand *et al.,* 1963.)

noted between the thirty girls proved to be correlated to their individual training volume: The girls who had trained hardest showed the most effective adjustments, and vice versa.

C. W. Zauner, A. E. Lorincz and L. F. Sterling (Proc. Research Section, Florida Convention, Amer Ass Health, Phys Ed and Recreation, Orlando, Florida, Dec. 3, 1966) communicated results of analyses of body composition of three outstanding girl swimmers age six years and nine months, seven years and four months, and nine years and eight months, who had participated in competitions for several years. Percentage values for lean body mass were 93.9 (as against predicted standard value of 76.4), 97.1 (against 77.8) and 94.9 (against 80.8). These values were the highest recorded for females and exceeded the values for the great majority of males. The authors wrote that "success in swimming depends more on strength than on buoyancy." The common belief that adipose tissue contributes to efficiency in swimming "because it aids flotation," is erroneous, they said. Upon expiration, good swimmers sink to the bottom of the tank. The most striking attribute of swimming champions is power.

The children were superior also in respect of their red blood counts, mean corpuscular volume and hemoglobin concentration. Their pulmonary diffusion capacity exceeded predicted values by about 100 percent.

Physical Growth, Psychological Maturation and Behavior

The first comparative studies of efficiency with special regard to the three basic components of physical performance, *viz.*, endurance, speed and strength, were conducted by Jokl *et al.* in the thirties. Standardized tests were applied to large numbers of children of between six and twenty years of age. Appropriate statistical procedures were used in the evaluation of the data. Figure 20 gives a graphic

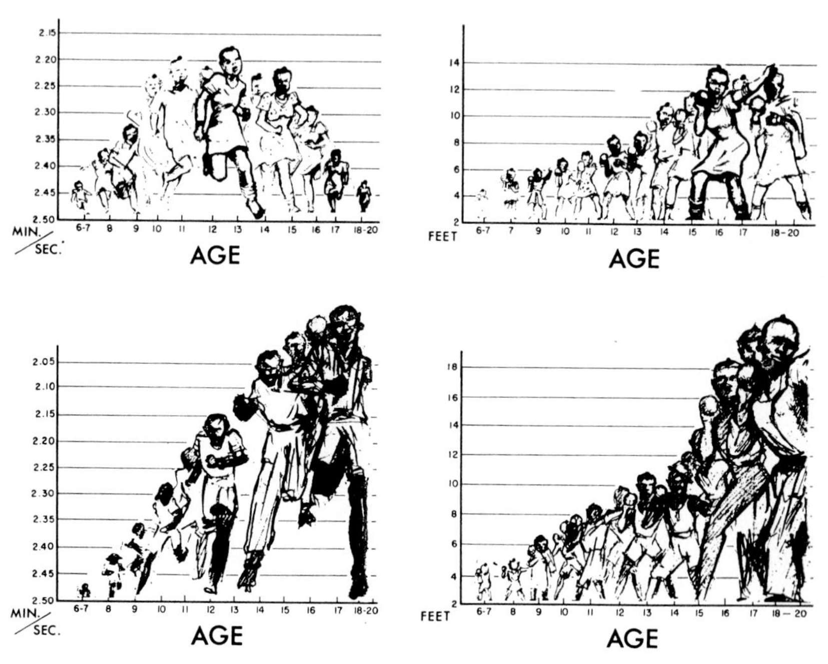

FIGURE 20. In boys, strength and endurance improve throughout maturation at about equal rates. Girls become stronger but fatigue more readily after puberty. This difference in patterns of functional development of boys and girls was shown in the African efficiency survey conducted with several thousand untrained children. Performances in shotput (*right*) increase at a similar rate in boys and girls even though boys are generally stronger than girls. A different picture emerges from the analysis of the data in the 600-yards running test (*left*). Here, the girls' performance growth arrives at a physiological maximum between ages 13 and 14 whereafter it tends towards a decline, while the boys' performances become steadily better until adulthood is reached. (Jokl, 1946 and 1949).

summary of differential growth patterns of boys and girls in respect of two tests, *viz.*, 600-yard running and shot put.

Mary Cover Jones and Nancy Bayley have analyzed the significance of acceleration of growth in terms of psychological maturation and of behavior. They examined two groups of boys who fell at opposite ends of a normal sample according to skeletal age determined from x-rays of the long bones of hands and knees. The sixteen most accelerated and the sixteen most retarded among ninety boys differed on the average by about two years in skeletal age (Fig. 21). The two groups showed a distinct divergency in sexual maturity. The accelerated boys were larger, of broader build, and stronger. They displayed good athletic abilities; the retarded boys were slender, long-legged, and gave low scores in strength and athletic tests.

As regards social attributes, the early maturing boys were rated as superior in physical attractiveness, personal grooming, cleanliness, attention to hair and nails, and neatness of clothing. The retarded

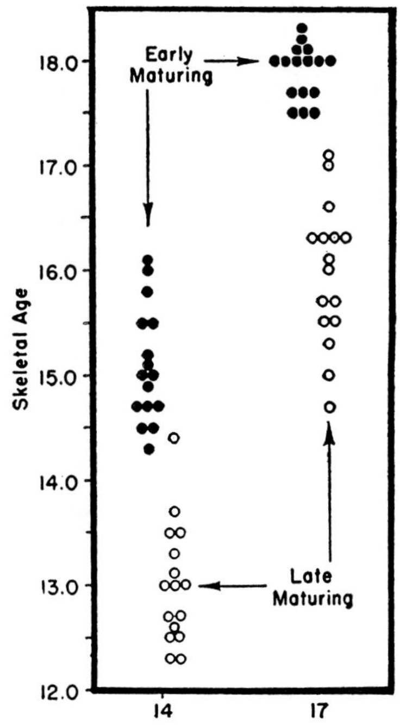

FIGURE 21. Skeletal maturity assessments of early and late maturing boys. Maximal difference in developmental age at chronological age of 14 is four years.

boys showed persistence of a childish activity pattern of which the authors say that "they may use it as the only technique they know to hold the attention of others and to compensate for a physically less favored status" (Fig. 22).

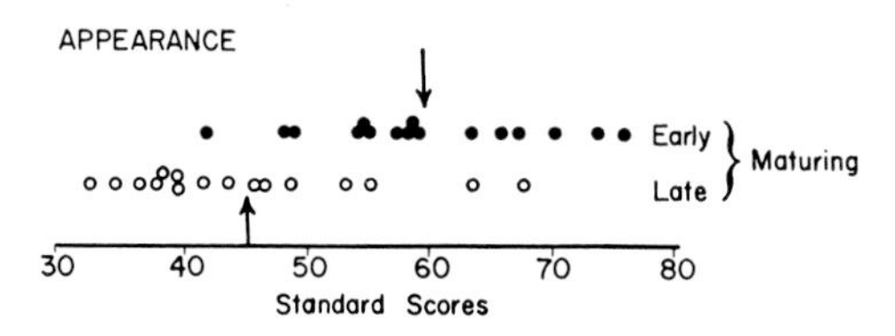

FIGURE 22. Comparative distributions of early- and late-maturing boys in appearance rating (Courtesy Mary Cover Jones and Nancy Bayley).

Deceleration of Aging

On the other end of the scale, Savolainen of Finland won a bronze medal in the gymnastics competition at Helsinki in 1952 at the age of forty-five; the Swiss 10-kilometer walking champion, Schwab, was forty-eight at the time of his start at the 1948 games; the third in the 50-kilometer walk, Johnson of Great Britain, was forty-eight; the second in the marathon, Richards, forty-nine; the hurdler, Finlay, forty. The French tennis champions Borotra and Cochet played in the finals of several international tournaments in 1954 when they were in their mid-fifties. At the age of forty-seven, Tilden beat the twenty-four-year-old champion, Don Budge. The British oarsman, Jack Beresford, fivefold Olympic winner in rowing, participated in a boat race on his fiftieth birthday. The Swiss mountaineer Chevalier of Geneva, climbed the Jungfrau when he was seventy-four years old. The forty-nine-year-old Tibetan Dawa Tondu was chief carrier for the British Everest expedition in 1953. Two former world record swimmers, Arne Borg of Sweden and Johnny Weismuller of the United States, swam the 100-meter in about 60 seconds when they were fifty years of age. The decline of "form" of ex-champions with age is usually due to discontinuation of training (Fig. 23).

The age range of participants in the Olympic Games in Japan extended from thirteen to sixty-six years. Half a century ago, such a span of maximal performance efficiency would have been unthinkable.

As a working hypothesis, the assumption may be made that sus-

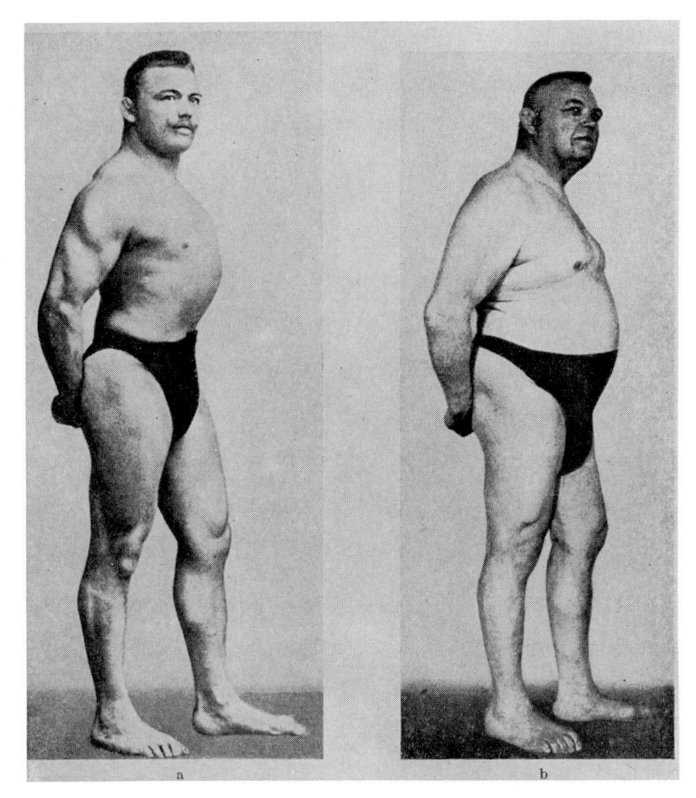

FIGURE 23. Internationally known wrestling champion at the height of his career at 28, and again at 63 when he had discontinued all training for more than 30 years. Deterioration of "form" is primarily due to cessation of exercise, not to "aging." (Courtesy F. Curtius.)

tained physical training inhibits all main facets of the aging process, namely the *decline of form,* the *decline of function,* and the *decline of health.* As regards the first, the changes of *body composition* which characterize "aging" may be conspicuous by their absence in trained old subjects. Old athletes, old lumberjacks, old mountain guides have been found to have a significantly greater lean body mass and significantly less excess fat than sedentary individuals of the same age. As regards the second facet, the *decline of function,* participants in the Annual National Gymnastics Festival in Germany, forty-eighty years old, were capable of physical performances demanding technical skill, cardiorespiratory endurance and muscular power equiva-

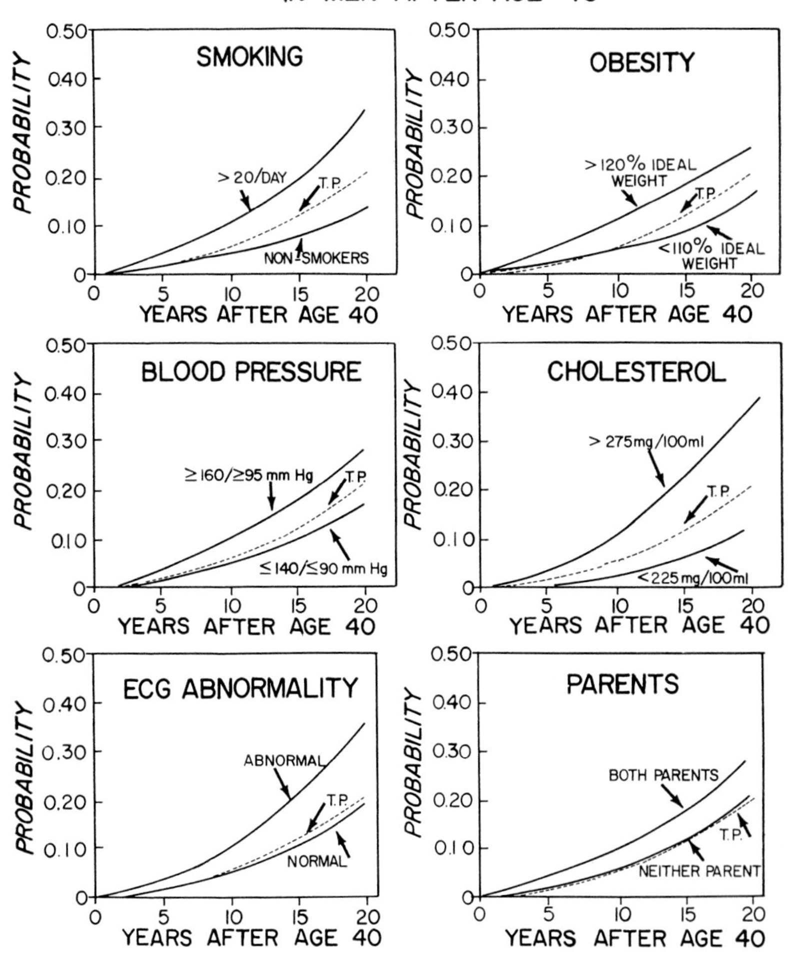

FIGURE 24. Effect of selected risk factors on the incidence of the following manifestations of coronary heart disease: sudden death, myocardial infarction with survival, angina pectoris, or an abnormal electrocardiographic response to exercise. T.P. = incidence rate of CHD in total population, approximately one percent per annum. Panel in lower right indicates the contribution to risk when heart disease of any sort is present in both parents. The curves are derived from life tables in which the probability of a man's developing CHD after the age of 40 is calculated from observations made over a ten-year period on a group of men ranging in age from 40 to 54 at the onset of the study. (Courtesy Kinch, S.H.; Gittelsohn, A.M., and Doyle, J.T.: Application of a life table analysis in a prospective study of degenerative cardiovascular disease. *J Chron Dis 17*:503, 1964).

lent or superior to those displayed by untrained young men. As to the third facet, the *decline of health,* Figure 24 depicts six major coronary risk factors which were identified in epidemiological studies. Since coronary heart disease is on the whole an affliction of middle and old age, the finding that some of the above risk factors can be "removed" through physical training, is of major importance. Significant increases of lean body mass and decrease of excess fat, to which reference was made earlier, significant increases of ballisto-cardiographically demonstrable systolic cardiac stroke force during systole, and significant lowering of blood pressure in hypertensive subjects have been demonstrated in longitudinal studies with young as well as with middle aged and old people.

Dimitrev's Study of Performances of Olympic Athletes of Over Forty Years of Age

Dimitrev has provided information on 987 men who at the time of their participation at Olympic Games between 1896 and 1964 were between forty and fifty-four, on sixty-seven men who were between fifty and seventy-three, and on eighteen women who were between forty and sixty-five years old. Three hundred twenty-one men took part in the *shooting* events, fifty-one of them obtaining medals, thirty-six placing fourth to sixth. Two hundred thirty-four were *fencers,* fifty-eight of them winning medals, thirty-one placing fourth to sixth. Two hundred seventeen competed in *yachting,* thirty-four among them becoming medalists and nineteen ranging fourth to sixth. One hundred seventy-one *equestrian* contestants won forty-nine medals (twenty-five gold, eight silver and sixteen bronze), and twenty-six came in fourth to sixth. Forty-five started in *track and field* events; among them were one gold, two silver and three bronze medalists, while three placed fourth to sixth. Of forty-one *gymnasts,* five won medals and five placed fourth to sixth. Thirteen entered *canoe-kayak,* eleven *wrestling,* ten *weight lifting,* eight *hockey,* six *water polo,* five *cycling,* five *rowing* and one the modern *pentathlon* competition. Twenty-one Olympic gold, twenty-one silver, and sixteen bronze medals in fencing were won by men of between forty and fifty-one years of age. A conspicuously large number among them were Hungarians.

Four Olympic competitions in which men as well as women of forty and older have competed with striking success were *fencing, yachting* (Fig. 25), *horse riding,* and *shooting.* As Table XI illustrates, the technical skills required for these sports may be acquired early in life but can be maintained or even improved over more than four decades.

FIGURE 25. The Enochina Yachting Harbor in Japan where the sailing competitions of the 1964 Olympic Games were held. Esthetically attractive and technically demanding, yachting is a sport in which sustained practice proves decisive. The age range of participants extended from 16 to 65.

Considering the continuous increase of ranges of age of Olympic competitors during the past decades, special interest attaches to Table X in which average ages of Olympic participants and of the six finalists, as well as the ages of youngest and oldest contestants and of

TABLE X

AGES OF PARTICIPANTS IN TRACK AND FIELD IN TOKYO 1964

	Average Age of Participants	*Average Age of First Six Finalists*	*Youngest*	*Oldest*	*Olympic Winner*
Men					
100 m	23.9	24.3	18	29	21
200 m	24.2	24.8	18	34	21
400 m	24.0	24.6	18	30	30
800 m	24.7	24.3	18	32	25
1,500 m	24.5	24.8	17	32	25
5,000 m	26.3	26.8	21	36	27
10,000 m	26.9	27.0	18	36	26
Marathon	28.0	27.7	19	36	32
20 km Walking	28.7	27.5	20	45	30
50 km Walking	29.5	28.1	22	45	31
110 m Hurdles	24.7	24.7	20	30	26
400 m Hurdles	23.4	23.8	20	30	24
3,000 m Steeplechase	26.1	26.8	18	36	27
High Jump	22.6	24.5	19	31	22
Pole Vault	24.7	25.3	16	32	23
Long Jump	24.8	23.7	21	37	22
Hop, Step and Jump	26.1	26.8	20	33	29
Shot Put	26.2	25.7	19	32	24
Discus	27.3	27.5	20	34	28
Hammer	28.8	28.1	19	43	31
Javelin	25.5	26.5	20	33	24
Decathlon	25.7	24.7	21	31	24
Tokyo 1964 (average age)	25.6	25.7	16	45	25.8
Rome 1960 (average age)	25.6	25.7			
Women					
100 m	21.9	19.8	16	32	19
200 m	21.9	21.3	16	32	20
400 m	23.0	26.0	17	36	26
800 m	23.9	24.8	17	36	22
80 m Hurdle	24.1	26.8	20	33	26
High Jump	22.4	25.1	17	28	27
Long Jump	22.6	22.8	16	28	24
Shot Put	24.9	26.7	19	33	27
Discus	25.6	29.0	17	35	27
Javelin	24.4	26.3	17	31	17
Pentathlon	23.8	26.3	18	30	25
Tokyo 1964 (average age)	23.2	25.0	16	36	
Rome 1960 (average age)	23.5	24.2			

Olympic winners in all track and field events in Tokyo 1964 are presented.

Table XI contains information on the ages of the youngest and oldest participants in fencing, yachting, equestrian and shooting competitions at the Olympic Games during the past fifty years, computed for all participants and for Olympic champions.

TABLE XI
AGES OF OLYMPIC GAMES PARTICIPANTS

	Participants			*Gold Medalists*		
Sports	No. of Participants	Minimum Age	Maximum Age	No. of Gold Medals	Minimum Age	Maximum Age
Fencing	1538	15	59	151	15	48
Yachting	74	13	63	44	16	59
Equestrians	713	16	72	64	23	56
Shooting	819	16	73	40	17	65

Ages of youngest and oldest participants in fencing, yachting, equestrian and shooting competitions at Olympic Games during the past 50 years, computed from all participants and for Olympic champions. Note the representation in the sample of boys of between 13 and 15 and of men of between 48 and 73 years of age. After Dimitrev.

Physique and Performance

The two most outstanding contributions to the understanding of the relationship between physique and performance have been made by the German psychiatrist Ernst Kretschmer and the United States Naval Surgeon A. R. Behnke. During the early twenties Kretschmer extended Kraepelin's classification of the endogenous psychoses into two main groups—dementia praecox and manic depressive madness—showing that these two forms of mental illness tend to be associated with different physiques. Patients afflicted with dementia praecox were usually lean, "asthenic" or "leptosome;" patients afflicted with manic depressive madness were well-rounded, "pyknic" (Fig. 26). This observation caused Kretschmer to attempt a classification of human physiques in general and to examine the question of whether a relationship also exists between mentality and body build in *normal* people.

> In the mind of the man-in-the-street the devil is usually lean and has a thin beard growing on a narrow chin, while the fat devil has a strain of good-natured stupidity. The intriguer has a hunchback and a slight cough. The old witch shows us a withered hawk-like face. Where there is brightness and jollity we see the fat knight Falstaff—red-nosed and with shining pate. The peasant woman with a sound knowledge of human nature is undersized, tubby and stands with her arms akimbo. Saints look abnormally lanky, long-limbed, of penetrating vision, pale and godly.

Twenty years after the appearance of Kretschmer's book *Physique and Character,* Sheldon undertook a subanalysis of the three somatotypes prescribed by Kretschmer. For each of them he defined additional physical features and correlated them with psychologically identifiable personality components. Both Kretschmer and Sheldon based their classification of somatotypes solely upon shape, not upon size. Thus two persons of similar body appearance are of the same somatotype even if one is twice as large as the other. For Kretschmer's terms "asthenic," "athletic" and "pyknic," Sheldon used the terms "ectomorph," "mesomorph" and "endomorph."

Body Composition

In 1942, A. R. Behnke presented evidence proving that a purely anthropometric approach to the study of human physiques is unable to yield information on the important factor of "body composition." In two classical communications he elucidated the relationship between specific gravity and fat content of the body, showing that obese subjects and exceptional athletes represent corresponding opposites in respect of the quantitative relationship of "lean body mass" and fat.

In accordance with Archimedes' principle, body volume can be determined by hydrostatic weighing to ascertain "equivalent volume" as the difference between a person's weight in air and in water. Corporeal density thus computed serves as an index of the amount of excess adipose tissue.*

The average weight in water of a group of twenty-eight obese men whose mean weight was 148.7 pounds and whose specific gravity was

*Weight in water is determined by suspending a subject below the surface of the water on a line leading to a spring scale graduated in ounces. A weighted lead belt maintains negative buoyancy for all types of persons, including very obese ones. Special methods are employed to measure vital capacity and residual air.

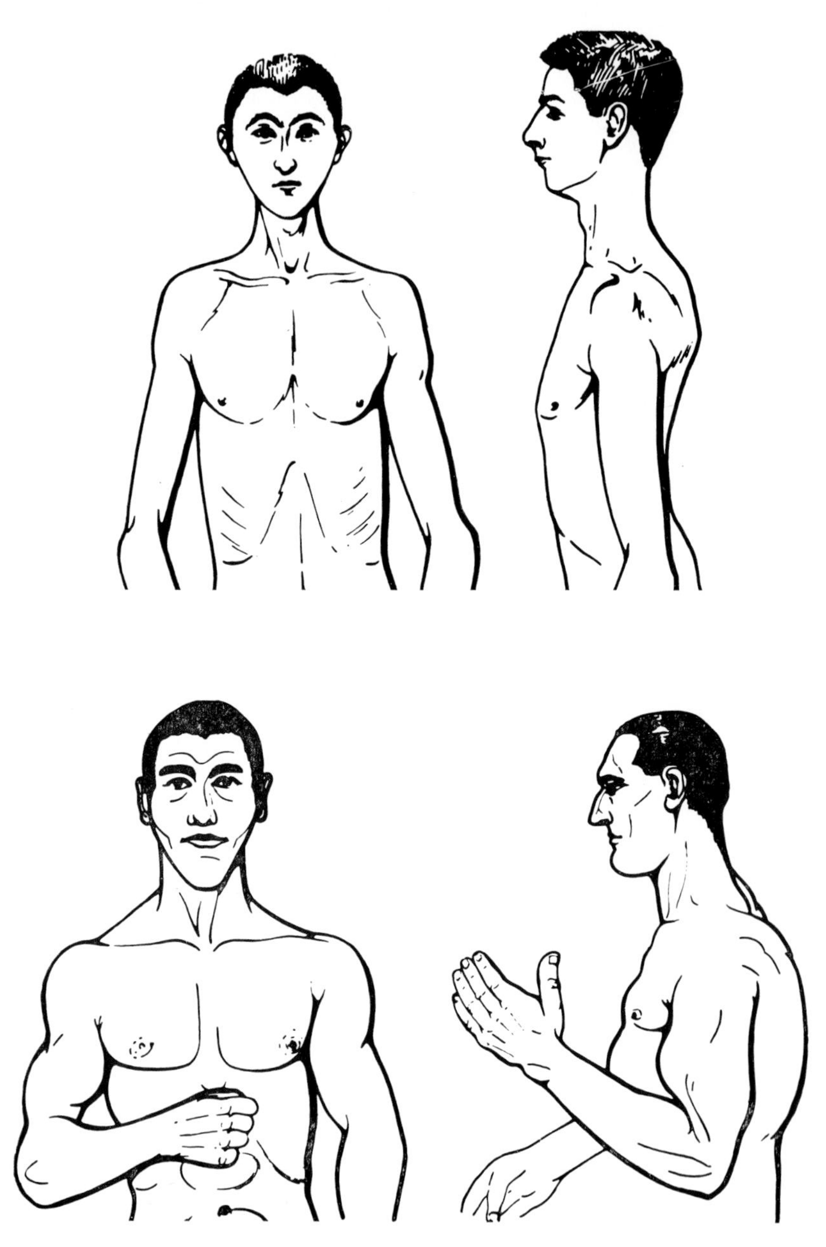

FIGURE 26. Kretschmer's three prototypes: (*A*) Asthenic; (*B*) Athletic; (*C*) Pyknic. (Courtesy E. Kretschmer, and Springer Verlag, Heidelberg.)

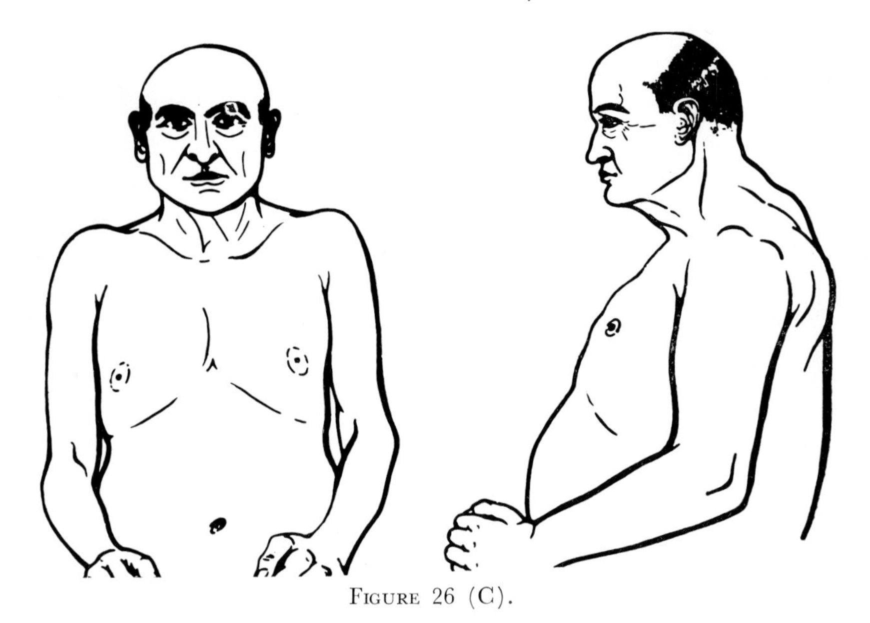

FIGURE 26 (C).

low (1.056) amounted to 9.4 pounds. The corresponding values for a high specific gravity group of thirty-eight fit men, whose mean weight was 176 pounds, were 1.081 and 11.1. The difference in weight in air between the two groups was 27.3 pounds.

On the assumption based on the above figures that a loss of 27.3 pounds of body weight in air is associated with a gain of weight in water of 1.7 pounds (11.1—9.4) the conclusion was drawn that if men in the low specific gravity group would have lost this amount, their specific weight would have risen from an initial value of 1.056 to 1.081; that is for every pound of weight lost the weight of the body in water would have increased 0.062 pounds. The specific gravity of the reduced tissues was calculated as 0.94. This value is in accord with the specific gravity of adipose tissue.

The difference between the specific gravity of the two groups was due to a variation in adipose tissue. The body may be viewed as comprising calcium salts (representing 50 percent of the weight of bone), essential or irreducible lipoid substance, excess adipose tissue and all other tissues of the body, embracing chiefly muscle, organs, brain, skin and blood. *The specific gravity of the mineral substance of bone is of the order of 3.0, adipose tissue 0.94, and all other tissue 1.060.*

In contrast with bone, the amount of excess fat is subject to wide variations. A value of 30 percent of the total body weight is not unreasonable for obese persons. For example, if a lean man weighing 140 pounds accumulates 60 pounds of adipose tissue, the specific gravity of the body will be lowered from 1.082 to 1.035. Since the density of the mass of tissue exclusive of bone and fat may be considered constant for healthy men, the *amount of fat appears to be the main factor determining specific gravity.*

Variations of Physiques of Untrained Subjects and of Athletes

Sheldon whose extensive researches have corroborated the validity of Kretschmer's original concept defined his system of somatotyping as ". . . a quantification of the three primary components determining the morphological structure of the individual." He tried to identify individual physiques through a series of three numerals, the first referring to "endomorphy," the second to "mesomorphy," and the third to "ectomorphy," each rated on a seven point scale, with *one* being the lowest and *seven* the highest rating. Half points were used for intermediate values on the rating scale. Endomorphy, the first component, was defined as "relative predominance of adipose tissue," mesomorphy, the second component, as the "relative predominance of bone, muscle, and connective tissue," and ectomorphy, the third component, as the "relative predominance of linearity and fragility."

Tanner's Contribution to Physical Anthropology

Tanner who has used Sheldon's system in several important developmental studies, presented in 1964 a monograph entitled *The Physique of the Olympic Athlete.* Figures 27 B and C (after Tanner) reflect the validity in physical anthropology of an observation made in 1942 by Behnke and subsequently elaborated by Brozek, Parizkova and Jokl to the effect that *body composition* of outstanding athletes is distinguished from that of nonathletes by the fact that they are not fat. At the same time it must be realized that athletes excelling in certain sports are morphologically differentiated from others who specialize in different athletic disciplines (Figs. 27 D-F). For example, as a group, outstanding shot putters are conspicuously tall and heavy; hurdlers are tall and slim; gymnasts are short and strong-

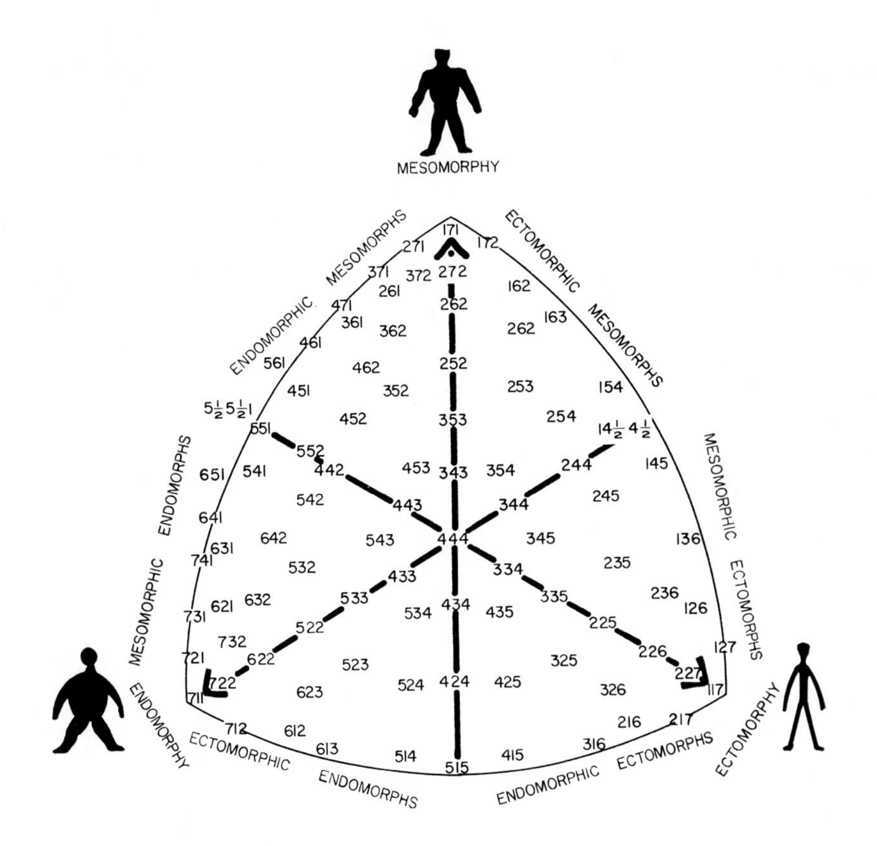

A. Chart for plotting somatotyes in two-dimensional diagram

FIGURE 27A-F. These figures, reproduced from Tanner's book, summarize the current status of sport typology. (*A*) shows the triangular design introduced by Sheldon, with "endomorph" physiques clustering toward the left, "mesomorph" toward the upper, and "ectomorph" toward the right apex. The results of Sheldon's survey of somatotype distribution of 4,000 male American college students in 1940 are shown in (*B*). Each dot represents 20 students. The concentric clustering around the 444 central crossing of the three hypotenuses of the triangle of the majority of the points, and the decreasing density of representation toward the three apices is evident. (*C*) shows the distribution of the somatotypes of 277 Sandhurst Military Academy cadets as reported by Tanner in 1952. A comparison of (*B*) and (*C*) indicates the trend of distribution of

————————>

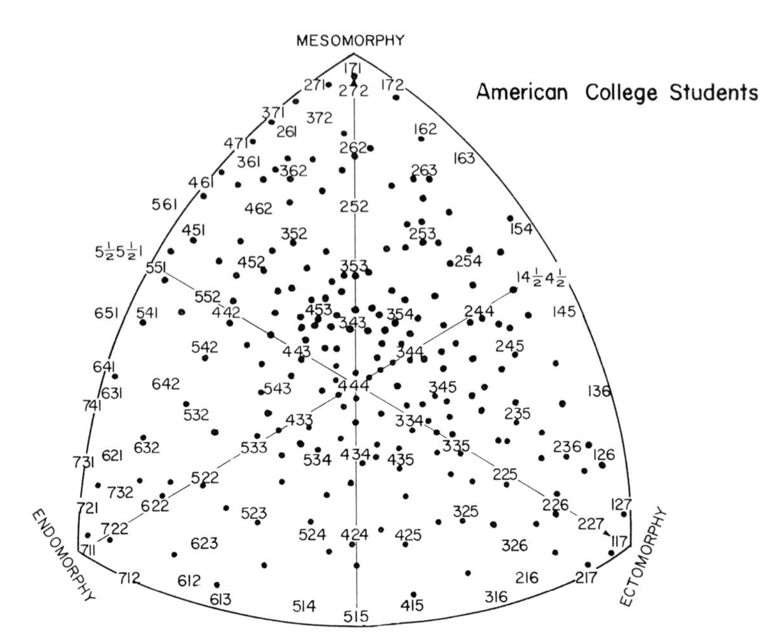

B. Somatotype distribution of 4,000 American College students Sheldon (1940). Each dot represents 20 students

the latter sample in the direction of the mesomorph, and less marked, of the ectomorph apices of the triangle. In (*D*) are plotted the somatotypes of 137 participants in the track and field contest of the Rome Olympic Games in 1960; in (*E*) and (*F*) highly selective samples of Olympic weight lifters and long distance runners. To reiterate, fat individuals are conspicuous by their absence among outstanding athletes, a feature which represents a common denominator of all first class performers irrespective of the nature of the athletic discipline in which they excel. However, within the anthropometric pattern thus defined differential anatomical trends are identifiable for various specialist groups as indicated by the clustering of the somatotypes of the Olympic weight lifters (*E*) toward the mesomorph, and of the Olympic long distance runners (*F*) toward the ectomorph pieces of the Sheldon grid. (Courtesy J. M. Tanner.)

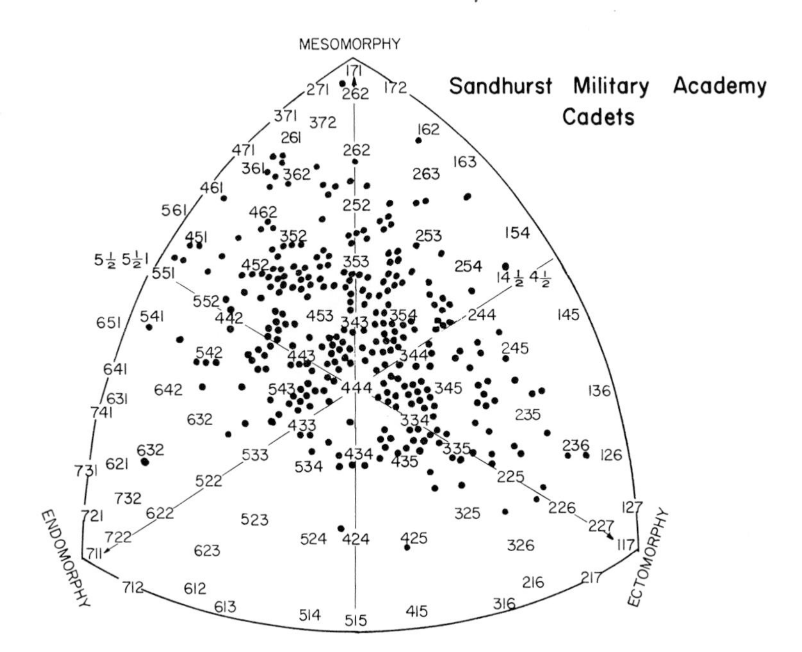

C. Somatotype distribution of 287 Military Academy cadets, 1952

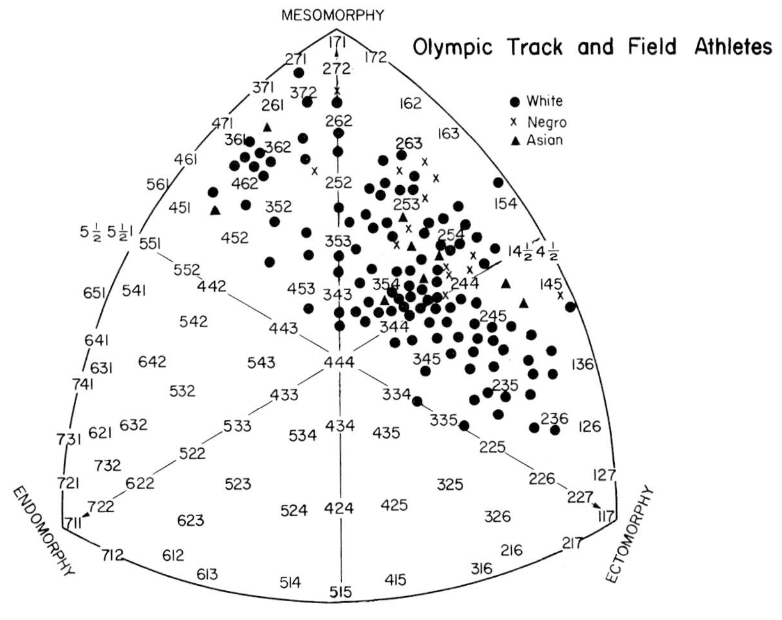

D. Somatotype distribution of 137 Olympic track and field athletes

FIGURE 27 C & D.

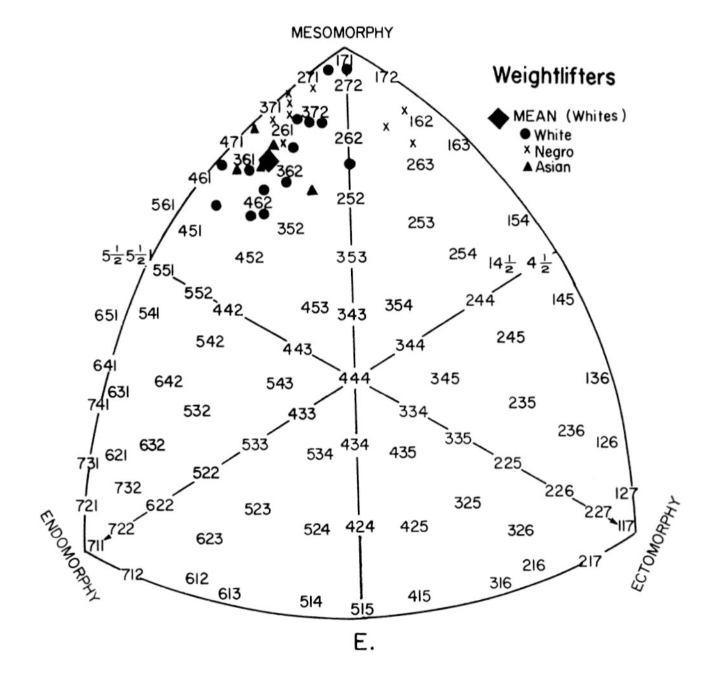
MESOMORPHY
Weightlifters
MEAN (Whites)
White
Negro
Asian
171
271 272 172
371 372 162
261 262 163
471 361 263
461 362
561 462 252
451 352 253 154
5½5½1 452 353 254 14½ 4½
551
552 442 453 343 354 244 145
651 541 542 443 344 245
641 642 543 444 345 136
631 741 532 433 334 235
632 533 534 434 435 335 236 126
731 621 522 225
732 226 127
721 622 523 325 227 117
722 524 424 425 326
711 623 216 217
712 612 613 514 515 415 316
ENDOMORPHY
ECTOMORPHY
E.

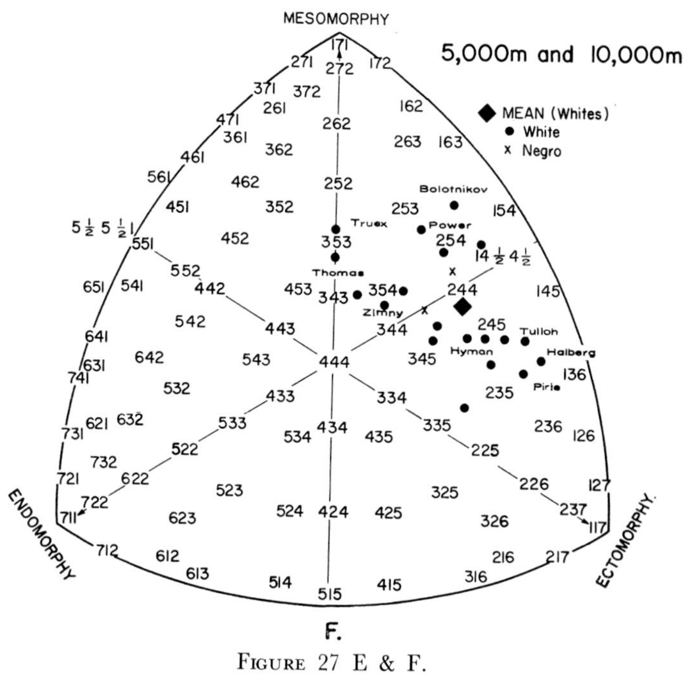
MESOMORPHY
5,000m and 10,000m
MEAN (Whites)
White
Negro
171
271 272 172
371 372 162
261 262 263 163
471 361 362
461
561 462 252
Bolotnikov
451 352 253 154
Truex
Power
5½ 5½1 452 353 254 14½4½
551
Thomas
552 442 453 343 354 244 145
Zimny
651 541 542 443 344 245
Tulloh
Hyman
Halberg
641 642 543 444 345 136
Pirie
631 741 532 433 334 235
621 632 533 534 434 435 335 236 126
731 522 225
732 226 127
721 622 523 325 237 117
722 524 424 425 326
711 623 216 217
712 612 613 514 515 415 316
ENDOMORPHY
ECTOMORPHY
F.

FIGURE 27 E & F.

armed; weight lifters are stubby and muscular; and long distance runners are lanky. None of them are fat.

Body Measurements as Determinants of Physical Efficiency

Figure 28 is based upon computation of 38,100 measurements of Swiss recruits during the Annual Army Induction Examinations in 1962. Body height was correlated with the results of four physical performance tests, namely climbing a rope 5 meters long, long jump,

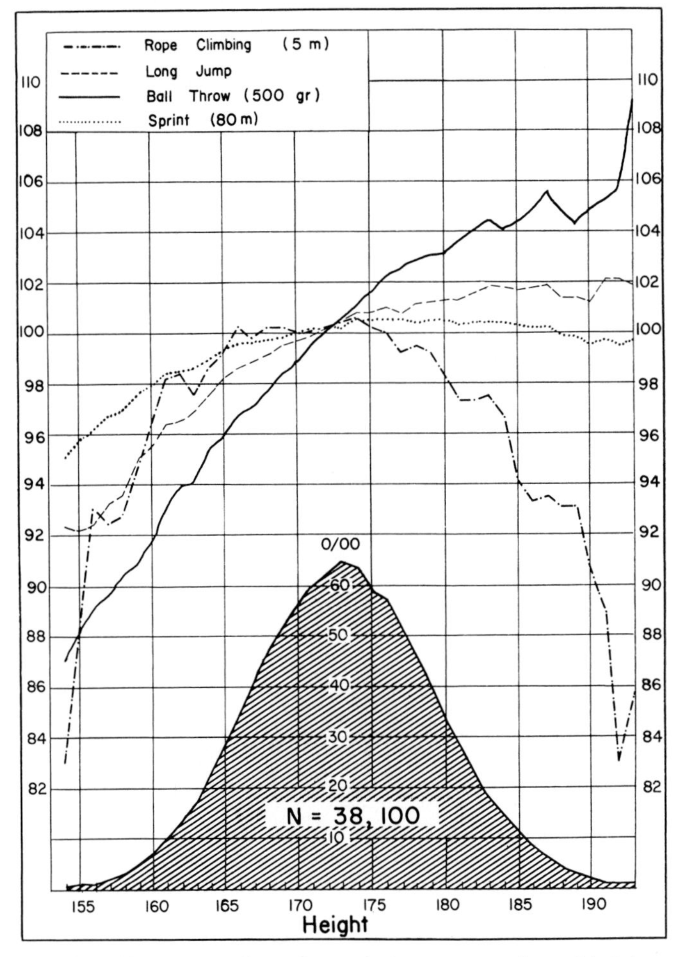

FIGURE 28. Graphic presentation of correlative computation of height and performances in 5 fitness tests conducted with 38,100 Swiss recruits.

TABLE XII-A

West Point

PHYSICAL APTITUDE EXAMINATION

GRADING SCALES

(cp. p. 85)

Score	*Standing Broad Jump*	*Modified Basketball Throw*	*Dips*	*Hurdle Run*	*2-Minute Sit-ups*	*250 Yard Shuttle Run*	*Score*
100	9′1″	95′	21	33″	75	44″	100
99		94′					99
98	9′0″	93′	20		74	44-1/5″	98
97		92′		33-1/5″			97
96	8′11″	91′			73	44-2/5″	96
95		90′		33-2/5″			95
94	8′10″	89′	19		72	44-3/5″	94
93		88′		33-3-5″			93
92	8′9″				71	44-4/5″	92
91		87′	18	33-4/5″	70		91
90	8′8″					45″	90
89		86′	17		69		89
88				34″		45-1/5″	88
87	8′7″	85′	16		68		87
86		84′			67	45-2/5″	86
85	8′6″			34-1/5″		46″	85
84		83′	15		66	46-1/5″	84
83		82′					85
82	8′5″			34-2/5″	65	46-2/5″	82
81		81′	14		64		81
80	8′4″			34-3/5″		46″	80
79		80′			63		79
78		79′	13	34-4/5″		46-1/5″	78
77	8′3″				62	46-2/5″	77
76		78′		35″	61		76
75	8′2″	77′	12			46-3/5″	75
74				35-1/5″	60	46-4/5″	74
73		76′					73
72					59	47″	72
71	8′1″	75′	11	35-2/5″	58		71
70	8′0″	74′				47-1/5″	70
69				35-3/5″	57	47-2/5″	69
68	7′11″	73′	10				68
67		72′		35-4/5″	56	47-3/5″	67
66	7′10″			36″	55	47-4/5″	66
65		71′					65
64				36-1/5″	54	48″	64
63	7′9″	70′	9				63
62		69′		36-2/5″		48-1/5″	62
61	7′8″				52	48-2/5″	61
60		68′		36-3/5″			60
59		67′	8		51	48-3/5″	59
58	7′7″			36-4/5″		48-4/5″	58
57		66′		37″	50		57
56	7′6″					49″	56
55		65′	7	37-1/5″		49-1/5″	55
54	7′5″	64′			48	49-2/5″	54
53				37-2/5″			53
52	7′4″	63′			47	49-3/5″	52
51		62′	6	37-3/5″	46	49-4/5″	51

Score	Standing Broad Jump	Modified Basketball Throw	Dips	Hurdle Run	2-Minute Sit-ups	250 Yard Shuttle Run	Score
50				37-4/5″			50
49	7′3″	61′		38″	45	50″	49
48						50-1/5″	48
47	7′2″	60′		38-1/5″	44	50-2/5″	47
46		59′	5	38-2/5″	43		46
45				38-3/5″		50-3/5″	45
44	7′1″	58′			42	50-4/5″	44
43		57′		38-4/5″		51″	43
42	7′0″		4	39″	41	51-1/5″	42
41		56′				51-2/5″	41
40	6′11″			39-1/5″	40		40
39		55′		39-2/5″		51-3/5″	39
38	6′10″	54′	3	39-3/5″	39	51-4/5″	38
37		53′		39-4/5″		52″	37
36	6′9″				38	52-1/5″	36
35		52′		40″	37	52-1/5″	35
34	6′8″			40-1/5″			34
33		51′	2	40-2/5″	36	52-3/5″	33
32	6′7″					52-1/5″	32
31		50′		40-3/5″	35	53″	31
30	6′6″	49′		40-1/5″	34	53-1/5″	30
29				41″		53-2/5″	29
28	6′5″	48′	1	33″		53-4/5″	28
27		47′		41-1/5″		54″	27
26	6′4″			41-2/5″	32	54-1/5″	26
25		46′		41-3/5″	31	54-2/5″	25
24	6′3″			41-4/5″		54-4/5″	34
23		45′		42″	30	55″	23
22	6′2″	44′		42-1/5″		55-1/5″	22
21					29	55-1/5″	21
20	6′1″	43′		42-2/5″	28	55-4/5″	20
19		42′		42-3/5″		56″	19
18	6′0″			42-4/5″	27	56-1/5″	18
17		41′		43″		56-2/5″	17
16	5′11″			43-1/5	26	56-4/5″	16
15		40′		43-2/5″	25	57″	15
14	5′10″	39′				57-2/5″	14
13				43-3/5″	24	57-4/5″	13
12	5′9″	38′		43-4/5″		58″	12
11		37′		44″	23	58-1/5″	11
10	5′8″			44-1/5″		58-2/5″	10
9		36′		44-2/5″	22	58-3/5″	9
8	5′7″					59″	8
7	5′6″	35′		44-3/5″	21	59-1/5″	7
6		34′		44-4/5″		59-2/5″	6
5	5′5″	33′		45″	20	59-1/5″	5
4	5′4″			45-1/5″	19	60″	4
3	5′3″	32′		45-2/5″		60-1/5″	3
2	5′2″	31′		45-3/5″	18	60-3/5″	2
1	5′1″	30′		45-4/5″	17	60-4/5″	1

throwing a ball weighing 500 grams, and a sprinting race over 80 meters. Very small young men are at a disadvantage in respect of all the performances under analysis; medium height (1.70 meters and 1.75 meters) is most favorable for good overall performances; tallness (1.85 meters and above) is a distinct advantage in respect of throwing performances, but a distinct disadvantage for climbing. Performances in sprinting and long jump are closely interrelated. They are independent of body height within the wide range of 1.70 meters to 1.95 meters.*

The above data were obtained from normal healthy young men, most of whom were not athletes in that they had not undergone intensive training for the performances in which they were tested. Comparison of the measurements obtained in 1962 with those recorded with earlier groups of Swiss recruits reveals the extent to which the *acceleration of growth* during the past six decades has affected the physical performance capacity of the population in its entirety. Table XII-A is of exceptional scientific value because very few standardized performance tests have been conducted over such long periods. The table demonstrates a functional improvement, the general direction of which was known, but the magnitude of which is certainly impressive. The 1905-1909 mean performance values for the eighteen-year-old youths were 2.85 meters for the long jump and 13.5 seconds for the 80 meter sprinting race, as against 4.49 meters and 11.1 seconds in 1962.**

In 1967, Montpetit, Montoye and Laeding (*Res Quart,* 2:231 ff., May) published results of measurements of grip strength of school children in Saginaw, Michigan, comparing data recorded in 1899 by A. Carmen with findings obtained by them in 1962-1963. The same grip dynamometer was used in both studies. Mean grip strength of children living in Saginaw today was found to be greater than it

*A. V. Hill (1925) pointed out that on theoretical grounds maximum speed in running should be independent of height. However, observations over the past four decades have revealed a tendency of the height of outstanding runners to increase with the remarkable increases of record performances that have taken place since 1925.

**Another important comparative computation contained in the 1962 Swiss Government Report is concerned with the chief diagnostic categories of finding during the medical examinations of recruits in 1888-1890 and 1962. Figure 29 is self-explanatory. Of special interest is the large incidence in the 1888-1890 sample of visual and auditory defects, of developmental retardation, and of goiter.

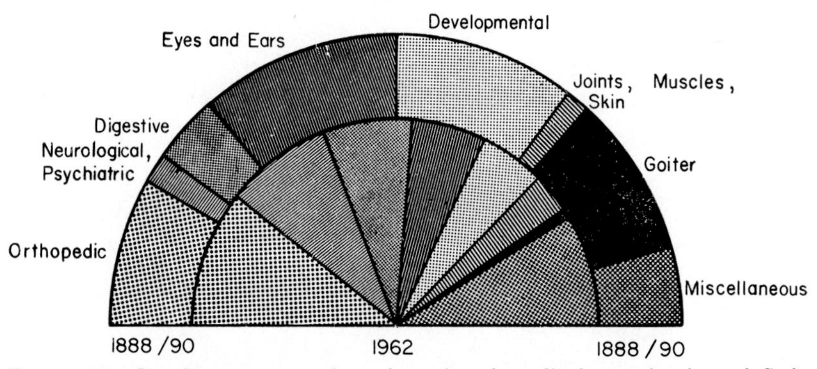

FIGURE 29. Graphic representation of results of medical examination of Swiss army recruits in 1888/90 and in 1962, classified according to diagnostic criteria.

was about seven decades ago, the difference being equivalent to about one and one-half years of development of strength during the age period twelve-seventeen, in boys as well as in girls. Interestingly, the authors found that grip strength of negro girls was about 2 kg greater compared with white girls, a fact of relevance for the interpretation of the data under study since in 1899 the school population of Saginaw was composed of 0.2 per cent negroes as against 27 per cent today.

Figure 30 shows differences in height of forty-eight high school boys, fourteen years of age. Since developmental status is a major determinant of learning capacity and physical performance, the issue is of major educational significance. Differences comparable in magnitude can be demonstrated in respect of many other morphological and functional features that influence athletic performances—of tallness for basketball, of muscularity for wrestling, of the size of hearts for long distance running, of intelligence for fine athletic skills, of high visual competence for manipulating small fast moving objects, of thermoregulation for swimming, and so forth.

The question has often been asked whether participants in athletic competitions should not be matched in accordance with their physical status, e.g., basketball players in accordance with their height, as contestants in wrestling, weight lifting and boxing are classified according to their weight. However, these proposals are not practicable. To implement them, it would be necessary to assess each individual's anatomical and physiological characteristics which simply cannot be done, certainly not on a mass scale. Furthermore, there is the fact that some outstanding basketball players are short, that not a few

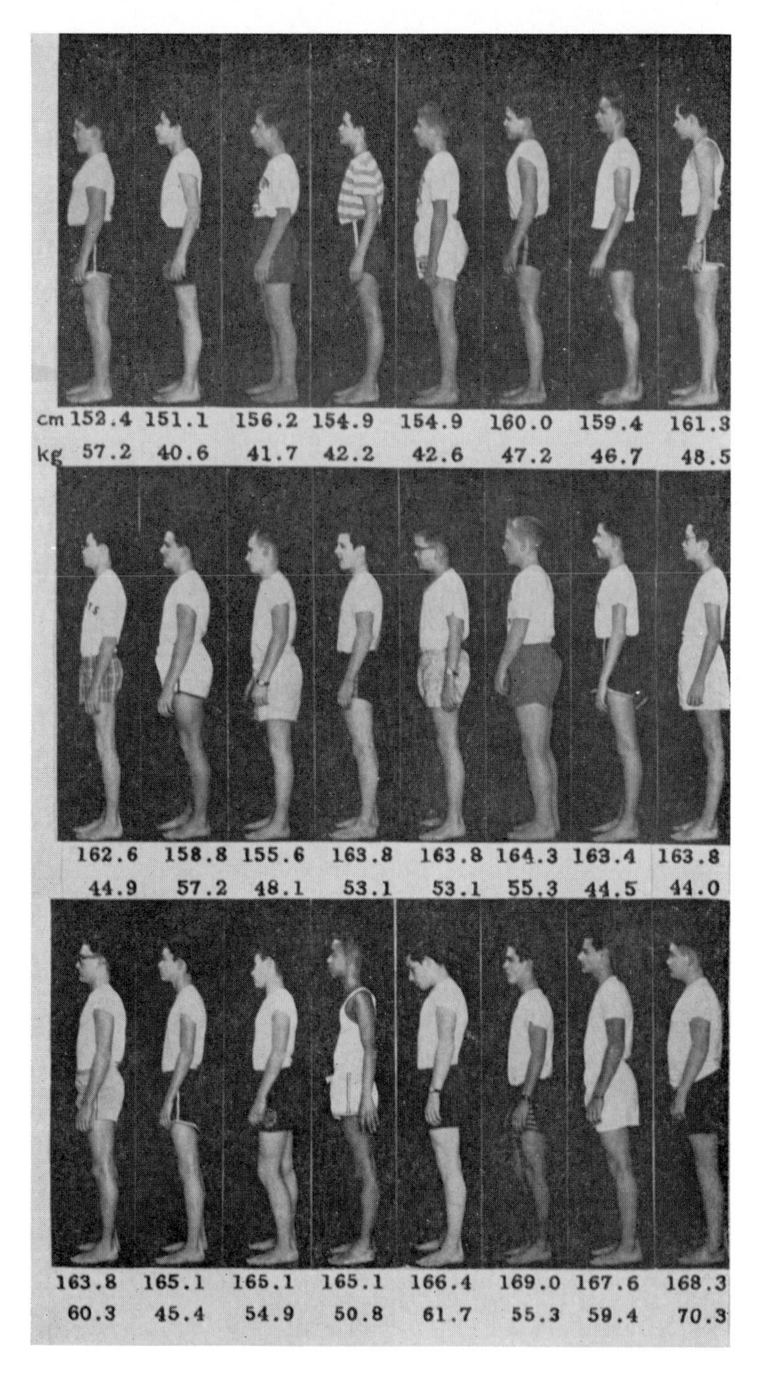

FIGURE 30. Lateral photographs of 48 boys 14 years of age taken at fixed distance with stationary camera. All negatives were printed by direct contact exposure to render individual pictures comparable. Mean height for the group

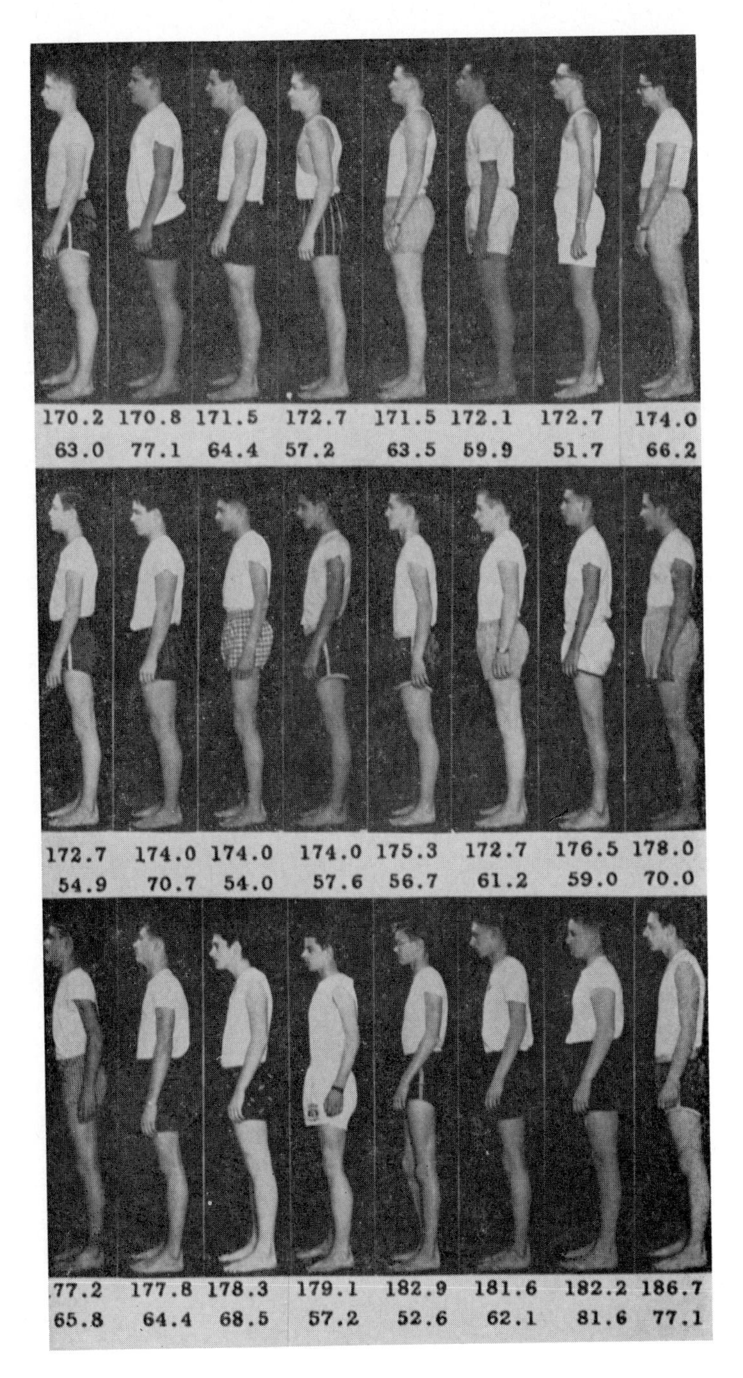

was 168 cm. The shortest boy measured 152.4, the longest 186.7 cm (range of weights extended from 40.6 to 81.6 kg). (Jokl *et al.*, Kentucky Physical Fitness Experiment.)

marathon runners have average sized or even small hearts (Fig. 31), that cases are known of intellectually underendowed youths excelling in feats demanding fine skill, and that serious refractory anomalies of the eyes do not render success in tennis impossible. The medical literature contains accounts of outstanding athletes who are afflicted with major orthopedic, neurological, or sensory afflictions. The whole issue is of special interest in that it reveals the integrative nature of the human performance.

(The issue has been studied in detail by Herbert Reindell of Freiburg, Germany to whom sportsmedicine is greatly indebted for a painstaking analysis of the physiological adjustments to exercise and training and their clinical implications. The evidence adduced by Reindell and his coworkers is presented in the following publications: Diagnostik der Kreislauffrühschäden, Enke, Stuttgart, 1949; 'Physiologische und pathophysiologische Grundlagen der Grössen- und Formänderungen des Herzens', and 'Das Sportherz', in Vol. IX/1, Handbuch der Inneren Medizin, Springer, Berlin, 1960; 'Das Intervalltraining,' Barth, München, 1962; 'Funktionsdiagnostik des gesunden und kranken Herzens,' Thieme, Stuttgart, 1967; Körperliche Aktivität und Herz- und Kreislauferkrankungen, Barth, München, 1966; and 'Die Belastungsinsuffizienz des Herzens,' Boehringer, Mannheim, 1965.)

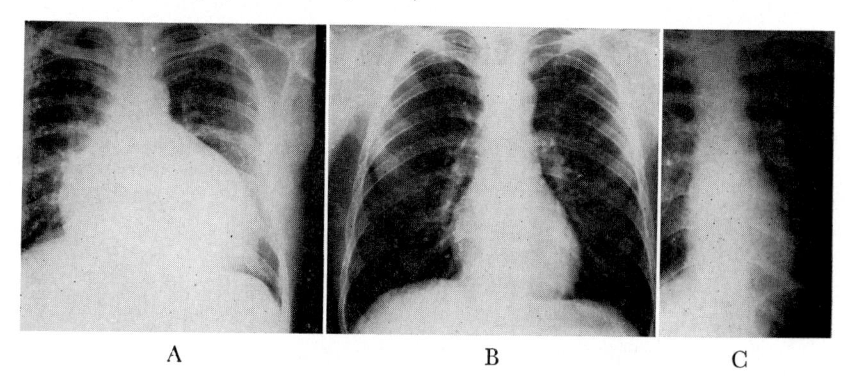

A B C

FIGURE 31. Teleroentgenograms of hearts taken at rest from three participants in the 1953 Pennsylvania Marathon Race. Each of them subsequently completed the 26-mile course. *(A)* shows a heart whose form and size are abnormal. The enlargement can certainly not be considered due to the endurance training. This man was free of symptoms of cardiac disease. The fact that he was able to compete in a marathon race is of considerable interest. *(B)* and *(C)* are normal hearts of different sizes as are encountered among well trained endurance athletes. While it is an established fact that long distance runners, swimmers, skiers and other endurance athletes have larger hearts than non-athletes, this statement is but of statistical validity. It need not apply to each individual case.

Chapter IV

ENDOWED AND ACQUIRED CHARACTERISTICS

To WHAT EXTENT are morphological characteristics of outstanding performers due to genetic endowment? How much can extraneous influences modify them? The preponderance of an anthropometric trait among successful athletes does not prove that this trait is the result of training: Basketball players are not tall because they play basketball, they play basketball because they are tall. Like considerations apply to the prevalence among outstanding gymnasts of men of short stature. On the other hand, the remarkable improvement during the past two decades of performance standards in all power sports is largely due to the introduction of strength training, e.g., isometric exercises and weight lifting.

However, it is necessary to point out that in every athletic discipline in which a given somatotype has been identified as a determinant of performance excellence, individuals with atypical physiques are at times successful. In 1948 Charles Fonville 1.88 meters (6′2″) tall and weighing 79 kg threw the shot 17.68 meters (58′⅜″) thus improving the world record held by Torrence Jackson 1.90 meters (6′2¾″) tall and weighing 138 kg.*

In my study of the Pennsylvania Marathon in 1954, I plotted the running times of the thirty-one participants against their somatotypes. Six runners were of asthenic, twenty were of asthenic-athletic body build (Fig. 34). As a group the former performed best.** Surprisingly, six had an athletic-pyknic physique. Even though their

*Fonville was also an excellent sprinter. So was Parry O'Brien, 1.90 meters (6′3″) tall and weighing 111 kg, who ruled supreme aming shot putters for more than twelve years. In 1954 he broke through the "60-feet barrier" with a throw of 60′ 5¼″ (18.42 meters). In the twentieth year of his competitive career, O'Brien improved his personal best performance to 64′ 7½″ (19.80 meters).

**Among outstanding middle distance runners there have been several powerfully built champion performers, e.g. Mills and Clarke. (See Figs. 32, 33 and Table XII-B.)

FIGURE 32 AND 33. The 10,000-meter final at Tokyo. Number 722 is Mills who won the event; number 12 is Clarke who reached his top form only after the Games when he established himself as the greatest long distance runner in the history of athletics so far. Of special interest is that both runners are conspicuously muscular, manifesting an anthropometric trend which

has been noticeable during the past decades in all athletic disciplines, notwithstanding the fact that sharp and categorically relevant differences of somatotype are demonstrable for champion performers in events demanding endurance or strength. Attention is drawn also to the fact that the best long distance runners today are significantly taller than their predecessors 40 years ago. (cp. Fig. 15).

TABLE XII-B
RECORDS SET BY RON CLARKE

Distance	*Location*	*Date*	*Time*
Junior Mile	Sydney	February, 1956	4 min. 6.8 sec.
10,000 meters	Melbourne	December, 1963	28 min. 15.6 sec.
6 miles	Melbourne	December, 1963	27 min. 17.6 sec.
3 miles (indoor)	New York	February, 1964	13 min. 17.4 sec.
3 miles	Melbourne	December, 1964	13 min. 7.6 sec.
5000 meters	Auckland	February, 1965	13 min. 33.6 sec.
10 miles	Melbourne	March, 1965	47 min. 12.8 sec.
5000 meters	Los Angeles	June, 1965	13 min. 28.5 sec.
3 miles	Los Angeles	June, 1965	13 min. 0.4 sec.
3 miles	London	July, 1965	12 min. 52.4 sec.
10,000 meters	Turku	July, 1965	28 min. 10.4 sec.
6 miles	Oslo	July, 1965	26 min. 47.0 sec.
10,000 meters	Oslo	July, 1965	27 min. 29.4 sec.
20,000 meters	Geelong	October, 1965	59 min. 22.7 sec.
One hour run	Geelong	October, 1965	12 miles, 1060 yds. — 1 ft. 10 ins.
2 miles (indoor)	San Francisco	February, 1966	8 min. 29.2 sec.
5000 meters	Stockholm	July, 1966	13 min. 16.6 sec.
3 miles	Stockholm	July, 1966	12 min. 50.2 sec.
*2 miles	Melun	June, 1965	8 min. 24.2 sec.

*Both Clarke and Michael Jazy of France broke the record although Jazy won the race. At the time of writing this monograph, Clarke ranks as the best long distance runner in the world so far. A statement of his records therefore seems to be relevent for the purpose of this survey.

mean running times were by far the slowest of those of the three groups (Fig. 35), the mere fact that these men were able to complete the 26-mile course is remarkable. Not more than one in 500,000 can run the marathon distance. Needless to say, all participants had indulged in long and strenuous practice prior to the race. Evidently, the effectiveness of sustained training as a means to engender endurance is very great. It goes without saying that *outstanding* performances over the marathon distance, e.g. running times under 2½ hours, presuppose intensive preparation as well as the possession of genetically endowed characteristics — most important among them an asthenic or asthenic-athletic physique, and exceptional cardiorespiratory resources. *No pyknic runner will ever win the Olympic Marathon.*

Likewise, a significant adaptive enlargement of the heart has been shown by several investigators to be a collective characteristic of athletes who excel in performances of endurance. Again, exceptions are encountered. In Figure 31 are shown the largest and the smallest hearts among thirty-one competitors of the Pennsylvania Marathon race referred to above. (As regards short term response of the size of the heart to the 26-mile race, see Fig. 36.)

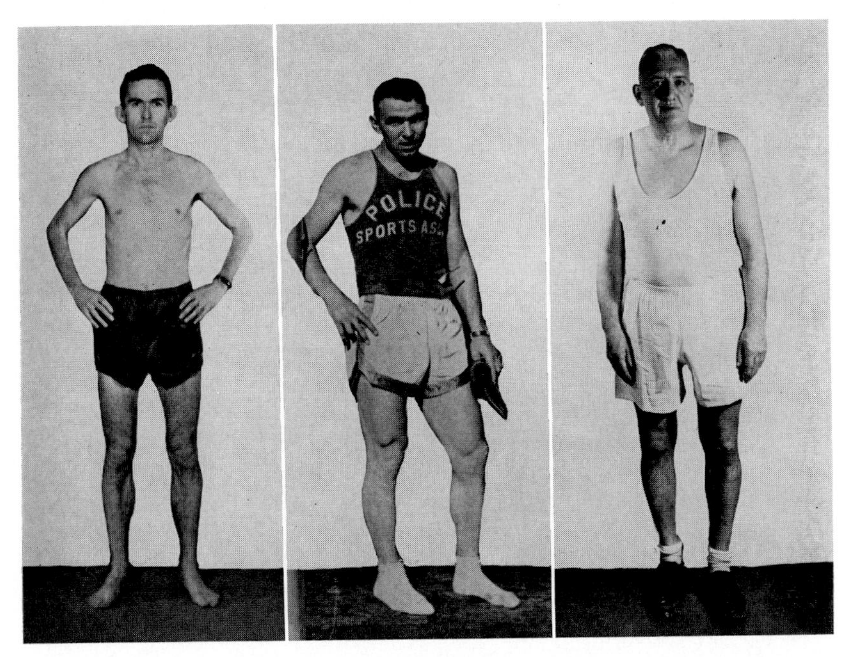

FIGURE 34. Three marathon runners all of whom finished the 26-mile distance. Each represents one of Kretschmer's prototypes—the one on the left is distinctly asthenic, the one in the middle, athletic, the one on the right, pyknic. Evidently, physique is not the only determinant of endurance, even in respect of performances of endurance as demanding as running over very long distances. According to J. Nason, sports editor of the Boston *Globe,* the lightest winner of the Boston Marathon was Kei Yamada (1953) who weighed 108 lbs, the heaviest Larry Brignolia (1899) who weighed 177 lbs. (The oldest winner was Clarence de Mar (1930) who was then 40, and youngest Tim Ford (1906) who was 18. The tallest winner was Joe Smith (1942) with 6ft 2in, the shortest Yun Bok Suh (1947) with 5 ft 1 in.)

Neurophysiologic and Autonomic Adjustments

These observations represent examples of a broad principle which reflects the integrative nature of the body's adaptability to the demands of exercise. This adaptability is demonstrable not only in respect of *anthropometric* but also of *neurophysiological* and *autonomic* phenomena, in healthy as well as in diseased subjects.

Several outstanding tennis players, among them two members of the United States Davis Cup Teams between 1950 and 1960 were afflicted with diabetes. It had previously been known that exercise

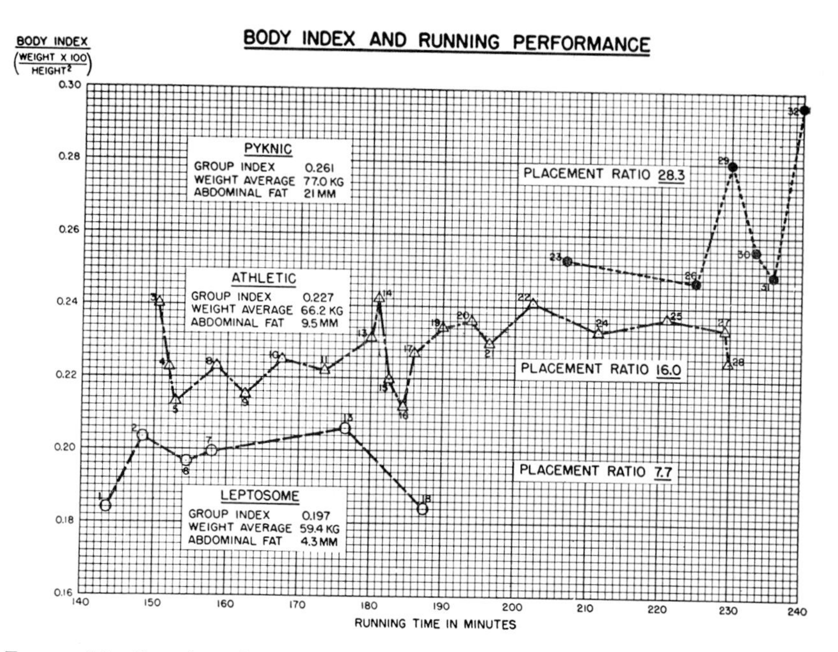

FIGURE 35. Running times of participants in marathon race plotted against body indices (abscissa) calculated from weight and height (ordinate) showing respective standards of physical endurance of thin (leptosome or asthenic) men as compared with muscular (heavier or "athletic") and with round (fat, broadly built or pyknic) subjects. That representatives of all three main body types were capable of completing a 26-mile race is in itself remarkable. Nevertheless body type is a determinator of physical endurance, even though it is not necessarily the decisive one: As a group, the "leptosome" runners were distinctly superior in running efficiency to the "pyknic," with the "athletic" body type in an intermediary position. Note the three performance averages for body indices, weight and abdominal fat layers. (The computation of body indices is a worthwhile procedure for pilot studies aiming at identification of correlative trends between body types and selected morphological and physiological parameters. Highly significant differences of ranges of body indices have been demonstrated for asthenic, pyknic and athletic sportsmen of comparable age.)

exerts a beneficial effect on the state of fitness of diabetics whose insulin requirements are thus reduced. However, it had been unknown that metabolic adjustment to training could enable diabetic "patients" to excel in international tennis tournaments.

Another category of observations pertains to champion athletes

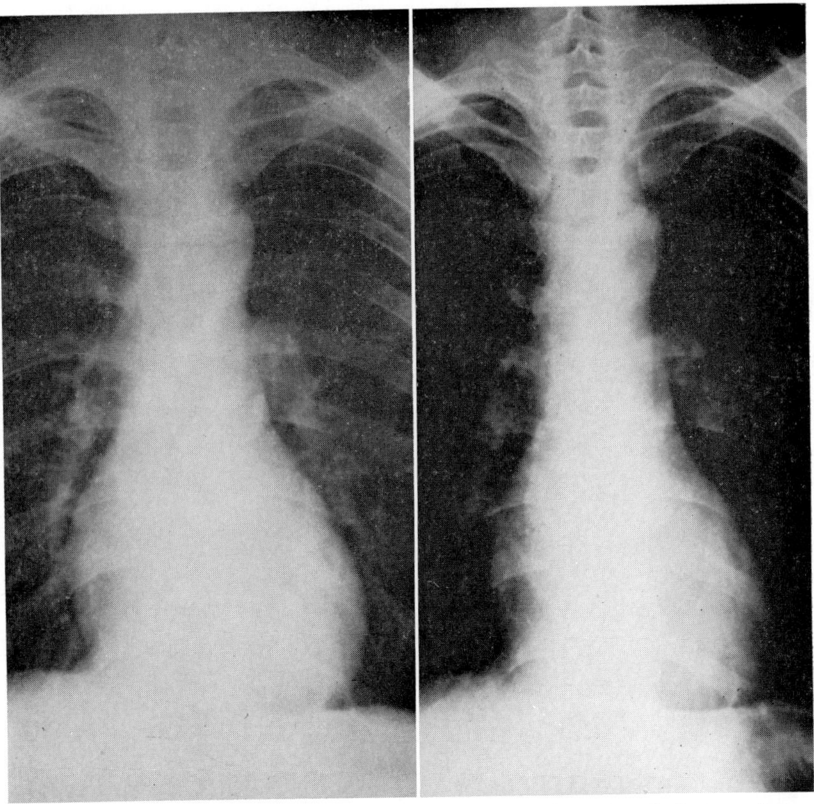

FIGURE 36. Teleroentgenogram of U.S. marathon champion before and immediately after race. The characteristic *diminutio cordis,* first described in 1921 by Deutsch of Vienna, is evident. The short term adaptive change in respect of the size of the heart of outstanding endurance athletes during a single protracted performance represents one of the most significant "heterostatic" deployment features. As Ernst Simonson pointed out in 1942, it is a seemingly paradoxical fact that the large heart of outstanding endurance athletes changes its action pattern during exercise in that its end-diastolic volume becomes smaller while its ventricular stroke volume becomes bigger. The reason is that during systole almost the entire residual blood is thrown into aorta and pulmonary artery. Reindell has shown that the heart of the untrained, as well as of the athlete who is not capable of feats of endurance cannot do likewise.

with cardiac disease. One of the greatest marathon runners in the British Commonwealth was accidentally discovered to be afflicted with a combined aortic and mitral valvular defect due to rheumatic fever. That this man became an outstanding contestant in long distance races indicates the extent to which functional adjustment of the circulatory system to training is possible.*

Ordinarily, hemoglobin values rise with acclimatization to altitude. However, Sir John Hunt, the leader of the British Everest Expedition of 1953, reported that two members of his team had abnormally low hemoglobin levels. Their physical performances on the mountain were exceptionally good.

Awareness, Knowledge and Motor Response

Athletes today compete not only against living contestants but also try to attain abstract goals in that they are aware of the existence of "optimal" standards in all measurable performances. In 1947 Bartlett pointed out that "it is not practice, but practice *the results of which are known* that makes perfect." In the early thirties Thorndike demonstrated an increase of accuracy in drawing lines blindfolded when the subject was told whether each attempt was too short or too long. *Without knowledge of results*, the subject showed no improvement; but he began to do so as soon as he was informed of the outcome of his efforts. *Knowledge of results* provides essential feedback. Baker and Young, and Bilodeau found that improvements of performances with knowledge of results occur in two stages. In the first, the approximate limits of the action are learned. In the second, finer adjustments are achieved. What is learned in the first stage survives the removal of knowledge of results. However, the fine adjustments of the second stage are quickly lost unless the subject is supplied with information of success or failure.

Empirically derived experiences in athletic coaching confirm the validity of these observations. For example, modern training methods of track runners include efforts to develop awareness of "tempo," a quality which may be named "chronoception." Outstanding middle distance runners can maintain for a given length of time a predetermined speed. The best among them do so within ranges of error of as little as one- or two-tenths of a second for 400 meters. Corresponding precision of awareness of success or failure in achieving motor tasks form part and parcel of practice in all competitive sports. It is thus that the gap between trying and achieving is eliminated. "Aim"

*Jokl and Suzman, Aortic regurgitation and mitral stenosis in a marathon runner. *J.A.M.A., 114*:467-470, Feb. 10, 1940.

and "feel" of any motor act become more and more alike in the course of purposively planned training. The latter presupposes a carryover of knowledge of results of one trial to the next.

The longer the time interval between two trials the greater the probability of the subjects' attention being distracted by other events. This is one of the reasons why all athletic training schedules to be effective must adhere to high levels of intensity, repetitiveness and variation.

In 1967, Welford* emphasized the importance of the quality of the data feedback. The more exact the knowledge given to the subject of the results of each of his actions, the more effective will his actions become over a series of trials. Lines drawn blindfolded by McGuigan's subjects were more accurate if they were told their error to the nearest 1/8 in. than if they were told only to the nearest 5/8 in. or 1 1/4 in. Also it is important that the information is clearly related to the action. Unduly complex information is ignored.

Coaching experiences confirm that discrepancies between what the athlete is required to do and what he has achieved must be brought to his knowledge promptly and in an understandable manner. Also, the process of control and information must be continuous. Thus, daily training is a prerequisite of motor learning. When knowledge of results is given and subsequently removed, performance deteriorates.

An important psychological determinant of *performances of long duration* is the maintenance of vigilance under monotonous conditions. When during the twenties the great Finnish athletes Nurmi and Ritola established their dominance in long distance running it was believed that running speed should be kept as constant as possible. We have learned in the meantime that this rule is not advantageous and that tempo changes are effective contributors to record performances. The vigilance or arousal effect thus introduced is of course not the only, and certainly not the primary facilitator. A number of physiological adaptations are essential prerequisites for the effectiveness of the psychological modifiers under discussion. To apply the classical dictum by the sixteenth century French philosopher Jean Fernel, the *physiological status* of the runner represents "the stage of the events;" the record performance is "the event itself."

*Welford, A. T.: The acquisition of skill. In *Readings in Physical Education,* edited by John E. Kane, London, Phys Ed Ass Gr Brit, 1966. (Contains excellent bibliography on psychology of sport.)

Finally, Welford deals with the fact that the *initial* attainment of reasonable competence at athletic, industrial, artistic and other skills is followed by a long period of further development during *continued* exercise of the skill. On the perceptual side, sustained practice enables the performer to select from among the mass of data impinging on his sense organs and he will neglect much of what is striking to an unskilled person. He will thus acquire the ability to react to data that a beginner fails to notice. We have emphasized this neurophysiological mechanism in our reports on record performances by physically handicapped athletes who had arrived at synthesis of motor patterns of great originality and effectiveness.* Because of the fact that these subjects' physical abnormalities rendered it impossible for them to emulate the standard techniques used by normal people—e.g., in the case of 1956 Olympic champion and long time world record holder in hammer throwing Harold Connolly whose atrophic and paralyzed left arm precluded his adopting textbook styles of hammer throwing—they were compelled to search for alternative motor designs. *In doing so they discovered superior designs of their own.*

Athletic Excellence and Social Status

The question arises whether superior physical performance capacity such as can be brought about readily through training affects personality development and social status of children. Ferenc Bakonyi (1964) of Budapest has studied the relationship between intellectual and athletic abilities of ten- to fourteen-year-old boys and girls, and their social status. Each of them was asked to name among his classmates the best friend, to choose a playing team, and to identify a child to whom he would entrust a secret. The information was correlated with data pertaining to each child's intellectual and athletic ability scores and to the friendship patterns within the group. *The best athletes and the best scholars had most personal friends, were most frequently chosen as members of a team, and most often considered worthy of sharing secrets.*

Bakonyi pointed out that the conspicuous popularity of the best athletes and of the best scholars suggests that these two groups possess

---

*Jokl, E.: Three olympic athletes. In *Conditio Humana,* Berlin, Springer, 1966, pp. 115-135.

a common feature which renders them attractive to the group. This common feature, he says, is *excellence of performance,* irrespective of its nature. Children of the age range under study desire to establish their prestige in order to give expression to their emerging personality. They evaluate their classmates in accordance with the same criteria.

As focal point of sociometric validation, *athletic* excellence exerts a somewhat greater attraction than *scholastic* achievement; while the athletically least competent children are the loneliest of all. The results of Bakonyi's analyses were identical for boys and for girls.

Physical unfitness and scholastic backwardness as primary determinants of a child's loneliness are remediable. More than any other known personality features, substandard neuromuscular and intellectual performance levels can be decisively raised through appropriate educational methods. Education will improve the mental competency of boys and girls even if their endowment is undistinguished, and in the weakest, the clumsiest and the fattest children sustained and intensive physical training establishes the morphological and functional prerequisites for participation in playing, swimming, running, hiking, mountain climbing, skiing, cycling, and boating as well as in a great variety of other activities. By enabling them to act as members of their group, physical training liberates these children from their isolation. Bakonyi's findings were corroborated in a paper 'Change in Sociometric Status during Military Basic Training related to Performance two Years later,' by Paul D. Nelson and Newell H. Berry (*J. Psychol, 61*:251-255, 1965.)

In her report of data obtained in a study of a large unselected group of obese children in the Department of Pediatrics at the College of Physicians and Surgeons in New York from 1937-1941, Hilde Bruch stressed that a high correlation was observed between inactivity of a fat child and his social isolation. Fifty per cent were both inactive, and without friends or playmates; seventy-four per cent did not take part in any group activities; sixty-five per cent had marked difficulties in social contacts by being oversensitive, sulking and easily hurt, or by bullying smaller children.

This capacity of sport at its best to establish a special kind of human relationships has far-reaching implications. Such relationships are accessible most readily through joint participation in situations

38
22
35
58
398
adidas

FIGURE 37. Rene Maheu, Director General of UNESCO, has said that like the art connoisseur, the spectator at a sporting contest is linked with the object of the event by a "current of sympathetic participation." In the theater as well as in the stadium an intense empathy develops between spectator and performer. "Spectator sports are the true theater of our day." Sport is able to release and, in the Aristotelian sense, to purge the emotions of the spectator just as effectively as any work of art in general, and the theater in particular. In reference to this close link generating a current of understanding and support from nameless crowds of watchers and listeners, to the individual taking the sporting stage and "expanding himself," Maheu says that it takes us back to the very start of the theater of antiquity, the theater of Greece. Like culture and the arts in general, sport exteriorizes the feelings and emotions of the player and causes the spectator to experience "catharsis," the purification of the soul of which Aristotle wrote long ago.

Lewis Mumford has pointed out that sport presents three main elements: the spectacle, the competition, and the personalities of the gladiators. "The spectacle itself introduces the esthetic element, so often lacking in the "paleotechnic industrial environment" itself. The race is run or the game is played within a frame of spectators, tightly massed. The movements of this mass, their cries, their songs, their cheers, are a constant accompaniment of the spectacle. They play, in effect, the part of the Greek chorus in the new machine drama, announcing what is about to occur and underlining the events of the contest. Through his place in the chorus, the spectator finds special release. He is now at one with a primitive undifferentiated group; he feels relieved from the passive role of taking orders and automatically filling them, of conforming by means of a reduced "I" to a magnified "it." In the sports arena the spectator has the illusion of being completely mobilized and utilized. Moreover, the spectacle itself is one of the richest satisfactions for the esthetic sense that the machine civilization offers to those that have no key to any other form of culture. The spectator knows the style of his favorite contestant in the way that the painter knows the characteristic line or palette of his master; and he reacts to the bowler, the pitcher, the punter, the server, the air ace, with a view, not only to his success in scoring but to the esthetic spectacle itself. This point has been stressed in bullfighting, but of course it applies to every form of sport."

While attending sporting events the "masses" experience a feeling of being liberated from the impersonal mode of existence which characterizes life in their new technological society with its mechanization of transport, the emergence of a white collar class of workers, the bureaucratization of daily routine, and the automatization of production.

Helmut Plessner has pointed out that the traditional pilgrimage to Mecca which until not so long ago necessitated several weeks of walking, can now be undertaken by plane within hours or minutes. The result is that "the pilgrim arrives at the Holy Shrine in advance of his mind." Similarly, modern labor no longer conveys the sense of satisfaction that once came with the completion of a meaningful task. Work on assembly lines in factories is repetitive, senseless and boring. The occupational situation of the majority of white collar workers is frustrating. The worker as a human being has become anonymous. Fragmentation of labor and depersonalization of the laborer engender powerful inner tensions.

Sport is capable of establishing a new balance vis-a-vis the inequalities that which involve highly differentiated movements of the kind that distinguish outstanding performances in sport. The issue does not confine itself to the educational problem dealt with in Bakonyi's study. Rather, it concerns the "pathic"* interplay between sportsmen on the one side and spectators on the other, bound to each other by a fascinating spell that is mediated through the "spectacle." The latter is characterized, as Buytendijk has pointed out in a brilliant analysis, by "the combination of complete freedom of movement and strict discipline of rules" without which no "play" is possible. Only thus can the lasting attractiveness of the athletic contest be understood, and with it the unique bond that exists between participants and onlookers (Fig. 37).

Buytendijk's analysis also renders possible an understanding of the unique values that attach to those disciplines of sport and athletics which enable men and women to participate actively until the end of their lives, such as gymnastics, mountaineering, ice-skating, swimming, equestrian events, shooting and yachting. For those who utilize the potentialities of these athletic activities, many physiological, sociological and psychological problems with which textbooks of gerontology and geriatrics deal at length do not exist. We have presented evidence pertaining to this important question (Jokl, Alter and Leistung, Springer, 1954). At the yachting competitions in Tokyo in 1964, the age span of participants—all of them distinguished by exceptional skill—extended over half a century (Fig. 25).

*E. Straus has distinguished between two kinds of relationship between individual and environment. One he calls "pathic," the other "gnostic." The term "pathic" denotes an attitude of mind in which actions are guided by emotion rather than contemplation, a condition of "being swept or carried away;" while "gnostic" refers to a nonemotional, "intellectual" approach which aims at facts, concrete things and distinct experiences.

are caused by the steadily progressing transformation of society. Like art, sport washes away from the soul the dust of everyday life. Sport renders possible the expression and satisfaction of many desires which the modern world awakens as well as represses—desires for recreation and social contact, for aggression and play, for self-assuredness and hero worship. True, athletics and sport are not the only means to attain such satisfaction, but they would seem to be among the most readily accessible and the most rewarding, for performers as well as spectators, though of course in a different way for the former than for the latter.

For the interpretation of Bakonyi's conclusions, certain findings obtained in Lewis M. Terman's psychological studies on "genius" are of relevance. Among Terman's highly selected subjects (all of them having I.Q. ratings of 140 and above) those who made use in life of their superior intelligence were compared *fifteen or more years after the initial tests* with others who had failed to do likewise. In accordance with criteria established to identify those who had or had not made "use in life of their superior intelligence," the subjects were classified into three groups, composed of the highest fourth (A), the middle half (B), and the lowest fourth (C). "Significant differences between groups A and C were found in a retrospect analysis of their childhood data in respect of emotional stability, social adjustments and traits of personality. In other words, fifteen or more years prior to the classification of the subjects on the basis of *adult* achievement, it was possible to discern personality differences in *childhood* that would later characterize the achievement of these groups."

Evidently, even among intellectually gifted subjects such as those studied by Terman, success in life is largely determined by identifiable emotional, social and personality traits. In all probability, the situation is the same in regard to subjects who are gifted in respect of motor skills.

Psychological Determinants of Physical Efficiency

Analyses of data obtained from three classes of cadets at West Point (1951-1955, 1956-1960, 1961-1963), comprising more than 10,000 young men, revealed a significant positive relationship between initial physical performance levels and leadership ability assessed three-and-a-half years later. At that time youths whose physical performance test results were rated as "poor" showed least satisfactory qualities as officer aspirants, and were most likely to fail to graduate for any reason, to resign or to be discharged (cp. Table XII-A).

"Physical ability," defined as the capability to execute tasks which a soldier must be able to perform in line of duty was measured in tests which included running, jumping, throwing, climbing and dodging. Five percent of the candidates failed to obtain passing scores and were rejected from the start. Those included under the heading "Failure to Graduate" comprised youths who were subsequently dis-

GRAPH I
FAILURE TO GRADUATE

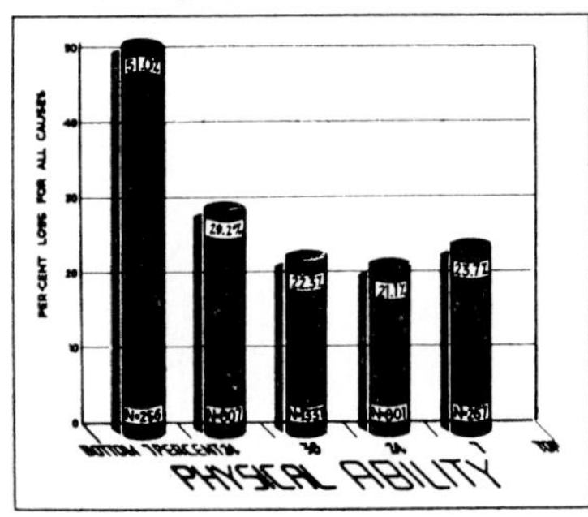

GRAPH II
VOLUNTARY RESIGNATION

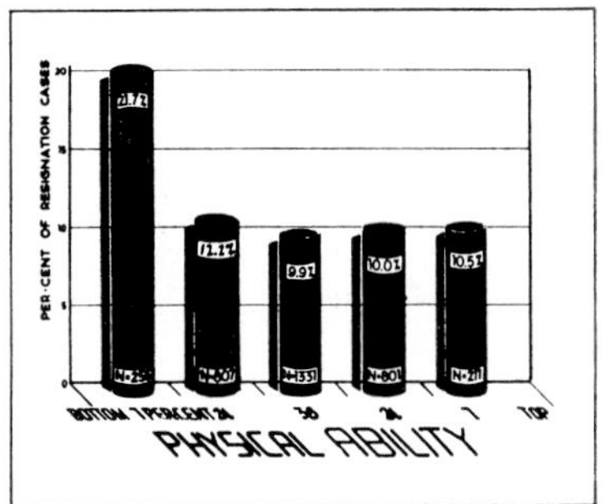

GRAPH III
OFFICIAL DISCHARGE

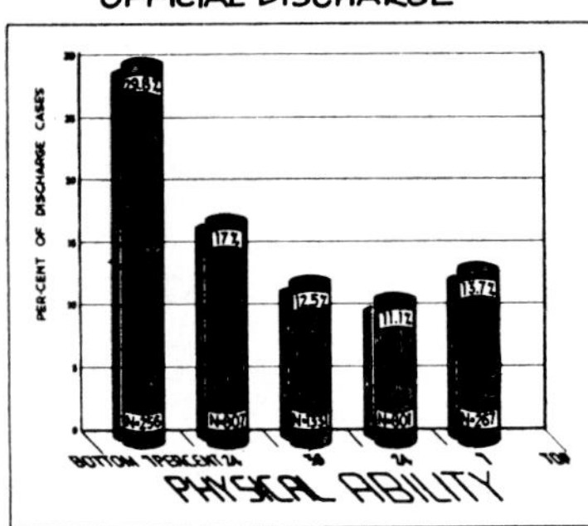

GRAPH IV
HIGH LEADERSHIP ABILITY WITHIN A CADET CLASS

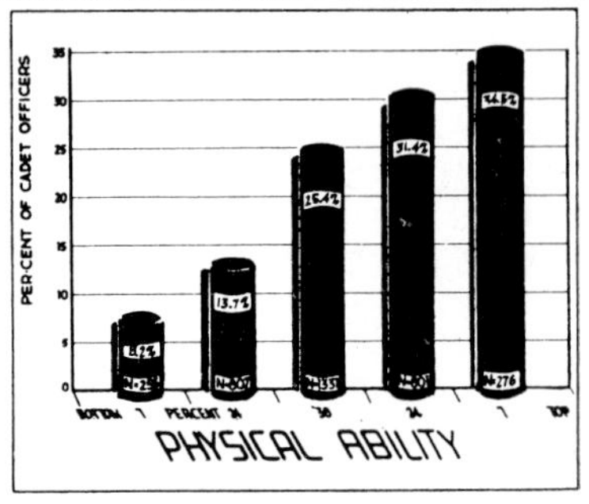

GRAPH V
LOW LEADERSHIP ABILITY WITHIN A CADET CLASS

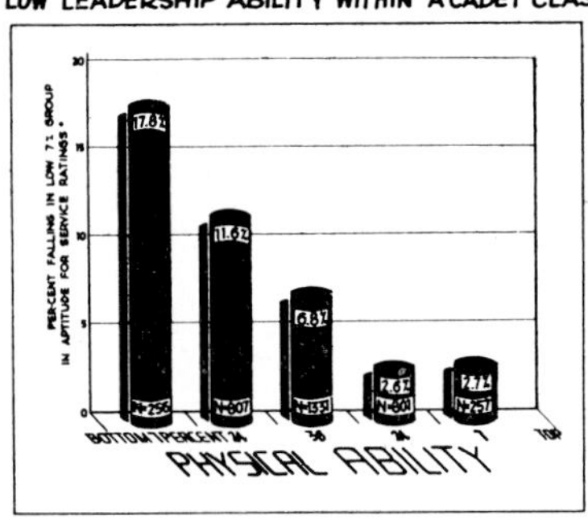

GRAPH VI
ACADEMIC FAILURE

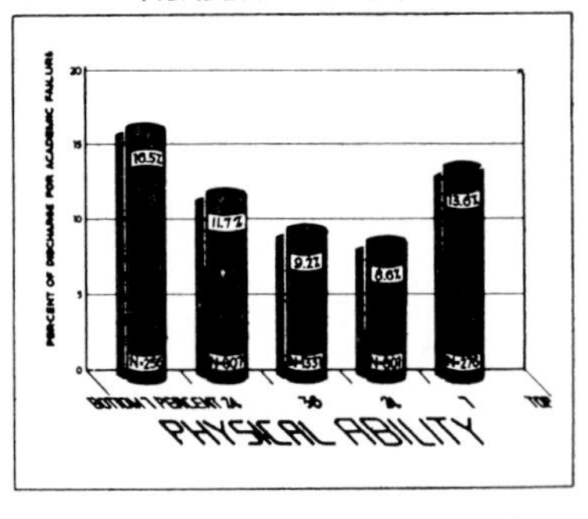

FIGURE 38. Analyses of data obtained from three classes of cadets at West Point (1951-1955, 1956-1960, 1961-1963) comprising more than 10,000 young men, revealed a significant positive relationship between initial physical performance levels and leadership ability assessed three-and-a-half years later. At that time youths whose physical performance test results were rated as "poor" showed least satisfactory qualities as officer aspirants, were most likely to fail to graduate for any reason, to resign or to be discharged. "Physical ability," defined as the capability to execute tasks which a soldier must be able to perform in line of

charged because of academic deficiencies, or for medical or administrative reasons, and those who resigned of their own volition. "Leadership," was identified as the ability to gain cooperation in efforts to achieve collective aims, measured through "peer ratings" as well as through "officers' ratings" (Fig. 38).

The validity of the above procedures was established in independent studies by the Personnel Research Division of the Adjutant General's Office with battle units in the Korean War.

Capacity and Ability

Blachowski (1964) emphasized that in all human performance studies a distinction must be made between *ability* and *capacity*. A child who is said to have the *ability* to speak French must be able to speak French. Children in countries other than those in which French is spoken do as a rule not have the ability to speak French even though most of them possess the capacity of speaking French. In other words, capacity is synonymous with readiness for use, while ability presupposes training. "In any line of activity—athletic, musical, literary, practical—individuals who have subjected themselves to the most intensive training come out with unequal abilities and we infer that they must have started with unequal capacities."

Jozef Pieter (1948) expressed the same idea by saying that "motor *capacities* are latent *potentialities* for given abilities." The former is always conjectural, the latter can be observed and measured. "An ability is invariably the result of training, and the degree of ability is related to the amount of that training."

Motor abilities are numerous. The question arises whether the

---

duty was measured in tests which included running, jumping, throwing, climbing and dodging. Five percent of the candidates failed to obtain passing scores and were rejected from the start. Those included under the heading "Failure to Graduate" comprised youths who were discharged because of academic deficiencies, or for medical or administrative reasons, and those who resigned of their own volition. "Leadership," was identified as the ability to gain cooperation in efforts to achieve collective aims, measured through "peer ratings" as well as through "officers ratings." The validity of the above procedures was established in independent studies by the Personnel Research Division of the Adjutant General's Office with battle units in the Korean War. (Courtesy Colonel Frank Kobes, Professor and Chairman, Office of Physical Education, United States Corps of Cadets, West Point, New York.)

number of motor capacities corresponds to that of motor abilities. We do not know. It is quite possible that every person is endowed with a "general motor capacity factor" comparable to the "general intellectual capacity factor" with which educational psychology operates. However, it is more likely that each individual harbors a number of independent motor capacities, e.g. those which determine strength, stamina and economy of movements, as well as corresponding capacities of the autonomic system, among them those which determine nature and scope of cardiovascular, respiratory, thermoadaptive and metabolic responses to training. Such capacities are in many cases amenable to identification through tests constructed in such a manner as to include the essential motor components that are required for a given task, as well as combinations and syntheses of movements whose effectiveness determines achievement and success in the field under reference (Fig. 39 A and B).

Motor Performance and Learning

It is within the framework of such considerations that the results of assessments of intellectual and learning capacities of physically trained and untrained children must be evaluated. In the Kentucky Physical Fitness Experiment a group of children participating in a high school exercise program of one full hour every day were compared with a nonactive group. The former's academic standing did not suffer notwithstanding the fact that their scholastic instruction schedule was curtailed because of the time requirements of their physical training program. Kruk-Olpinski (1964) scored results of general knowledge tests with 6,032 pupils in secondary and vocational schools. He found a slight superiority of "athletic" over "nonathletic" children. In another study covering 2000 boys and girls, half of them trained, the latter turned out to be the better learners. Finske and colleagues (1959) carried out an investigation of knowledge levels of ninth grade secondary school children comparing matched sample groups with two, three and six hours of physical training per week, respectively. He obtained low positive and low negative correlations, that is, the most highly trained children scored highest.

> The fitter pupils have in general results in learning no worse than those less fit, and the daily physical education lessons do not constitute

any danger for the progress in the other subjects, something of which school authorities are frequently afraid.

Mental Stability of Athletes

James S. Davie of the Mental Hygiene Clinic of Yale University reported in 1956 that the clinic sees significantly fewer athletes than nonathletes. His study is of major relevance since it identifies a number of personality and behavior patterns of patients and nonpatients

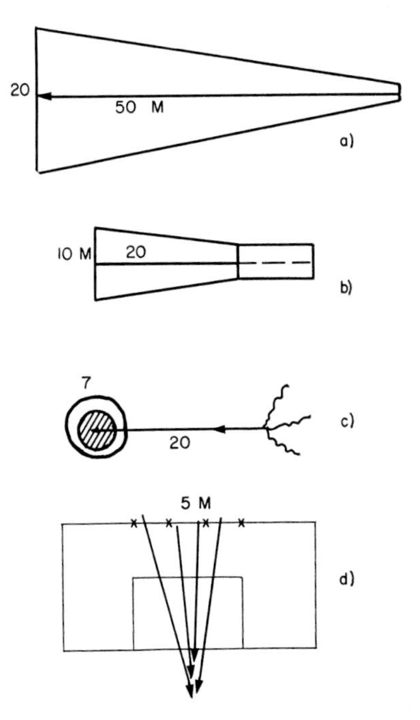

FIGURE 39A. Special procedures aiming at the identification of individual performance aptitudes for different sports have been elaborated. Zelenka has introduced a battery of tests suitable for application with 16-year-old boys to assess their potential skill in playing soccer. This figure illustrates four standard tasks. First, the ball is to be kicked so as to hit the point marked by the tip of the arrow. The distance between subject and point is 50 meters (a). Secondly, the ball thrown towards the subject is to be "headed" toward a target at a distance of 20 meters (b). Thirdly, the ball is to be kicked toward a target placed at a distance of 20 meters (c). Lastly, the ball is to be kicked so that it passes through hoops held in different positions (d). Each of the four tests is amenable to quantitative evaluation. (Courtesy W. Zelenka.)

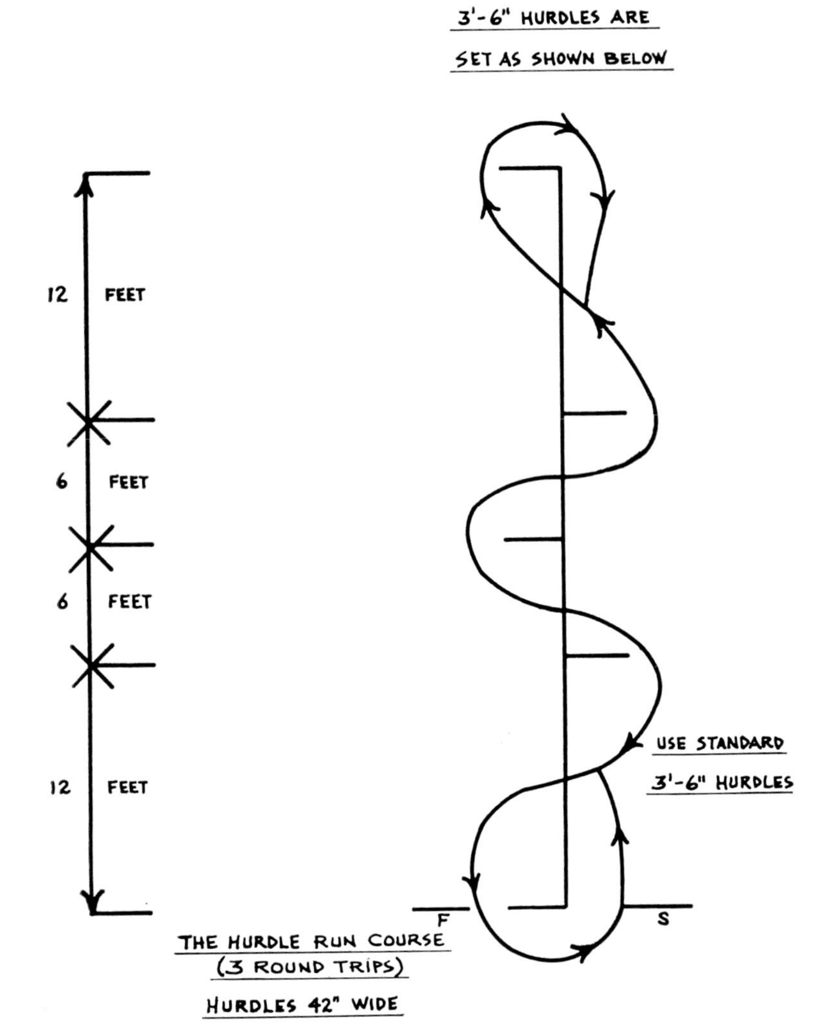

FIGURE 39B. Example of precisely laid-out standardized performance test for annual entrance examinations at West Point, New York. (Courtesy Colonel Frank Kobes, Professor and Chairman, Office of Physical Education, United States Corps of Cadets, West Point, New York.)

which allow essential differences between the personality structure of the two groups under reference to be recognized.

Compared with the nonpatients, the patients reported they had other than a very good time at secondary school, other than a very or fairly good time at Yale, and were in other than very or fairly good spirits most of the time at Yale. They were more likely to describe themselves as agnostic or atheistic or as having no religious preference. They had more visits also to the *medical* division of the health department and were in the *infirmary* more often. They were bothered more often by feelings of nervousness and loneliness while at Yale, felt out of place frequently or most of the time, had considered leaving Yale for another college, and felt that their college experience would have been more enjoyable in a smaller college and in a coeducational college. They participated little in athletics, and, when describing what they liked most about their experience at Yale, failed to mention the social-interpersonal-extracurricular side of college. They were more likely to write in criticism of their experience at Yale. They felt they had not lived up to what their fathers expected of them and, in general, reported having quite a bit of trouble adjusting to both the academic and nonacademic phases of college life at Yale. In brief, the patients appear to have had more trouble with their adjustment to college and to have felt their college experience unsatisfactory. Taken together, most of the differences suggest a *general syndrome of neurotic complaints.*

By contrast the nonpatients tended significantly to describe themselves as dependable, calm, prompt, and self-controlled and to deny being scattered, smug, worrying, dissatisfied, highstrung, idealistic, nervous, rebellious, and tense; while the patients looked upon themselves as anxious, moody, procrastinating, restless, sensitive, dissatisfied, highstrung, idealistic, nervous, rebellious, and tense. They did not consider themselves as consistent, efficient, relaxed, calm, prompt, and self-controlled. Compressing the list by looking at those adjectives which the students accepted as true, nonpatients described themselves as calm, prompt, and self-controlled while the patients denied this. In plain language, those who came for advice to the clinic had more troubles and self-concerns than those who did not.

In interpreting the clinical evidence one has to ask whether the greater mental stability of the athletes—Yale students are a highly selected group of gifted U.S. young men—relates to an exceptional sample with special attributes, or whether the findings point towards a cause and effect relationship between intensive physical training and the physiological, psychological and social situation thus engendered, and to the personality structure of the group of athletes revealed by the comparative analysis of the clinical data at Yale. Davie asks whether athletes are more "problem-free," or whether they have as many problems as the nonathletes but attempt to sublimate them through athletic activity; what role the coach plays in their lives, and whether he is functioning, consciously or not, as a therapist. The answer to all these questions is in the affirmative even though there can be no doubt that both genetic and extraneous influences contribute in greatly varying combinations to the development of the individual personality.

Davie's results were corroborated in a supplementary study conduced at West Point. The percentage incidence of cadets who were discharged or who resigned for psychiatric reasons during their four years' academic course at West Point was greatest in those whose standard score rating at the entrance physical aptitude tests was lowest, and vice versa. A significant preponderance of young men showing emotional maladjustment to the West Point environment was found among the bottom 7 percent category while not a single student in the top 7 percent sample was discharged with psychiatric endorsement (Fig. 40).

Therapeutic Implications of Psychosomatic Interrelations of Adjustments to Training

Wittich has paid attention to what he calls the "multifactorial interdependence of psychological and somatic manifestations of neurocirculatory asthenia." He has elaborated therapeutic procedures based upon the assumption that "restitution of an adequate physical performance capacity in this category of cardiac patients is an indispensable prerequisite for the initiation of meaningful psychological treatment." He points out that the majority of patients with neurocirculatory asthenia show distinct morphological and functional anomalies revealed by roentgenological and ergometric studies. Their cardiac measurements are conspicuously small, and their oxygen intake capacity is reduced. Neither the application of *exercise* nor *psychological* treatment *alone* is capable of producing satisfactory therapeutic results, while the combination of the two techniques under reference has proved to be effective. He demonstrated that physical

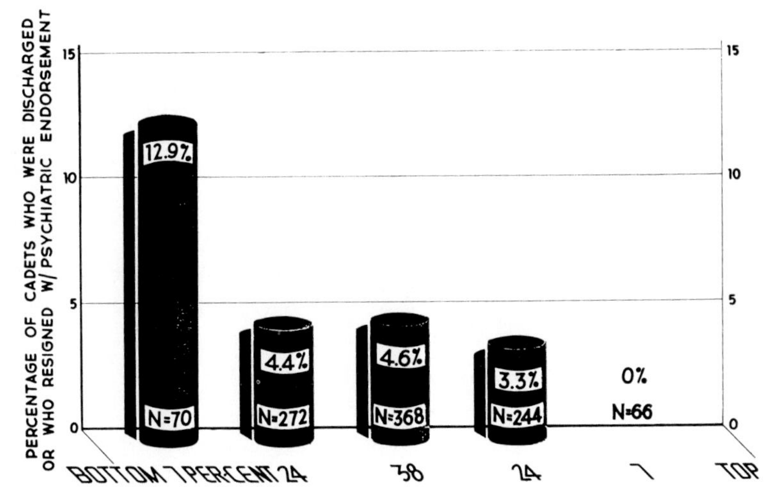

FIGURE 40. The percentage incidence of cadets who were discharged or who resigned for psychiatric reasons during their four years' academic course at West Point was greatest in those whose standard score ratings at the entrance physical aptitude tests were lowest, and vice versa. A significant preponderance of young men showing emotional maladjustment to the West Point environment was found among the bottom 7 percent category while not a single student in the top 7 percent sample was discharged with psychiatric endorsement. (Courtesy Colonel Frank Kobes, Professor and Chairman, Office of Physical Education, United States Corps of Cadets, West Point, New York.)

training leads in these patients to a significant *increase of cardiac stroke volume* at rest and during exercise, *ergometrically identifiable improvements* of maximal oxygen intake, and measurable *physical performance rises*. Wittich writes that pari passu with these physiological adjustments the patient becomes liberated from his *"anxiety through the heart,"* and thus from his *"anxiety about the heart."* This observation, he adds, is all the more noteworthy since in subjects with neurocirculatory asthenia intensive physical training is apt initially to "activate a high potential of anxiety," presumably because it "challenges and provokes a threatening rebellious and therefore vulnerable vital organ." In such situations the patient projects his feeling of discomfort upon his mother or others close to him. Continued physical training is likely to reassure him. The exercise stress confronts him, often for the first time, with an *internalized* object which he can identify. The result is that conflicts which hitherto he had been unable to comprehend become amenable to a rational solution. This is why the psychotherapist's effort benefits from the *combined* treatment program. Patients with neurocirculatory asthenia are usually disinclined to exercise. This fact distinguishes them from many categories of subjects with *organic* heart disease. Under the impact of exercise, psychotherapy and sociotherapy, this disinclination—almost invariably due to repression of infantile anxieties—disappears. The patient gains a new kind of knowledge of himself with the result that he accepts criteria by which to evaluate his condition. He takes cognizance of and is interested in many of the adaptive changes that establish themselves during training, e.g. his cardiac rate at rest and during exercise, the reduction of fatigue and of the feeling of discomfort caused during the early stages of the exercise program.

A sustained exercise program causes progressive physiological, psychological and social changes which psychotherapy alone is unable to engender. Physical training combined with psychotherapy is the procedure par excellence for the management of patients with neurocirculatory asthenia.

Physiological Considerations

For a better understanding of some of the so called psychosomatic sequelae of exercise, it seems appropriate to draw attention to a hitherto neglected aspect of ergometric research.

In interpreting the significance of the increasingly high maximal oxygen uptake values of trained subjects, emphasis has so far been laid almost exclusively upon energy production and utilization in terms of *muscle contraction.* The magnitude of energy that is required to produce the *electrical output of neurons* has received but scanty consideration. However, there can be no doubt that the implications of the enhanced oxydation potential brought about by training, at rest as well as during exercise, is of major relevance for the understanding of the problem of 'fitness,' including the psychological accompaniments discussed on p. 85 ff. The metabolic activity of the brain can best be visualized by comparison with the oxygen uptake of the constantly beating heart.

Of the 250 ml per minute of oxygen that is consumed by the body as a whole when at rest, the *heart* utilizes 22 ml per minute. In the same length of time, the *brain* utilizes more than twice as much, or 57 ml per minute. The *liver* and *intestines* use 50 ml per minute; the *kidneys* 18 ml per minute.

The weight of the brain is approximately four times that of the heart. Thus, the heart utilizes about twice as much oxygen per gram of tissue as does the brain. Nevertheless, even on this unit-of-weight basis, the *brain's oxygen utilization* is enormous, being 3.5 ml per 100 gm of tissue per minute, or *ten times that of the body as a whole.* This supposedly "inactive" organ, weighing only two per cent of the entire body weight, utilizes *20 per cent of the total oxygen uptake.*

Moreover, the requirement of oxygen to supply the metabolic needs of the brain is not affected by rest. While it is reduced considerably by narcotics and when in coma, oxygen uptake is essentially unchanged in sleep. This is in sharp contrast with skeletal muscle, which requires about 50 ml of oxygen per minute when at rest, but as much as 3,000 ml/min during strenuous exercise. *From a metabolic standpoint, the brain never rests.*

Another aspect of the brain's dependence on a constant supply of oxygen-rich blood is the relative paucity of its blood supply as compared with the oxygen uptake. The 20 per cent of the body's entire oxygen consumption which is utilized by the brain is obtained from only 15 per cent of the cardiac output. Thus, there is a greater extraction of oxygen from each unit of circulating blood. As a result, *the oxygen content of venous blood as it leaves the brain is lower than from any other organ except the heart.* (The $p0_2$ of venous blood from the liver and intestines is 45 mm Hg; from the kidneys 62; from the brain 35 mm Hg; and from the heart 18 mm Hg.) This would indicate that tissue oxygen tension is also lower than in other organs, thus increasing vulnerability to hypoxia, whether caused by circulatory or pulmonary embarrassment. (*CIBA,* Clinical Symposia, July-December 1966, pp. 77, 78.)

Chapter V

GENETIC DETERMINANTS OF ATHLETIC STATUS

THAT HEREDITARY FEATURES may determine physical efficiency was first suggested by the observation that certain families produce a succession of outstanding athletes. Many examples can be quoted. Two generations of Kellys of Philadelphia won Olympic medals in rowing —John Kelly Senior in 1920 at Antwerp, and John Kelly Junior in 1956 in Melbourne. F. Skobla Senior of Czechoslovakia won an Olympic weightlifting championship in Los Angeles in 1932; Skobla Junior became European shot put champion in 1958. She son of the 1925 German shot put champion, L. Lignau, established a new national record in the same event in 1960. The outstanding performances in swimming of the two Konrads, Jon and Ilsa, of Australia, and of Tamara and Irina Press of the Soviet Union in track and field are well known.

An approximate assessment of the degree to which endowment affects choice of and success in sports in adults was attempted by L Gedda in a study of two hundred twenty Italian national champions who came from families of whom two or more members had attained athletic distinction. The genetic influence of the common parentage in this selected group was more marked in some sports than in others. It was greatest in fencing, boxing, and shooting, smallest in soccer, gymnastics and track and field. In the latter sports, training is therefore relatively more effective than it is in the former.

The first quantitative estimate of the relevance of endowment over environmental influences in the development of motor efficiency resulted from the application of tests with identical and nonidentical twins, four and five years of age, by A. N. Mirenva of the Laboratory of Genetic Psychology in Moscow. Inter-twin differences of physical performances were found to be consistently greater in dissimilar than in similar pairs. After the weaker partner of each pair had participated over several weeks in daily exercise lessons, significant performance gains led to a distinct superiority of the trained over the untrained children. In other words, training had overruled endowment.

The effect of physical training upon growth and development was studied by O. von Verschuer and by H. H. Newman in several pairs of identical twins of whom only one member had engaged in exercise. For example, an outstanding gymnast weighed more and had stronger muscles, wider shoulders and less fat than his identical twin brother who led a sedentary life. Newman took measurements from identical twins who had been brought up in different homes. Among them was a pair of girls, one of whom worked on a farm while the other was a music teacher. The former's musculature was much bulkier than the latter's. If both identical twins follow the same athletic training schedule, no significant differences will be in evidence. In a pair of girl twins who had completed a 4 year physical education course, I found corresponding physiques as well as performances, both of the superior standards that generally distinguish athletic from nonathletic subjects.

The most extensive investigation of the role of genetics in athletics was conducted in 1960 at the Institute Gregor Mendel in Rome, with 1195 pairs of identical and nonidentical twins. The material was divided into three groups: In the first, both twins practiced sport; in the second, only one twin practiced sport; and in the third, neither twin practiced sport. Virtually no dissimilarities were found among the similar twins in respect to sport practice; that is both of them did or did not go in for athletics. On the other hand, in 85 percent of the nonidentical twins discrepancies were in evidence in regard to participation.

This differential result reflects the overwhelming influence of endowed drives in situations in which the choice is left to the individual whether to exercise or not. For the twins of group one, that is of those in which both members practiced sport, Gedda ascertained what kinds of sport they had selected (for example, weightlifting, track and field, soccer, and so forth). Furthermore, their athletic specialties (sprinting, hurdling, long distance running, or, in team sports such as soccer, their position) as well as performances were identified. This subanalysis also revealed categorical differences between the identical and nonidentical twin athletes. Synonymity of activity patterns was very great among the identical twins, while considerable differences were encountered in the nonidentical pairs. Almost all members of the identical twin group not only practiced sport, but they also practiced the same sport; while among the members of the nonidentical twin group who had been selectively chosen because both members did participate in sport, rates of coincidence were as low as 22 percent, as against over 70 percent for the identical twins.

If both were active in athletics, many of the nonidentical twins preferred different sports and their performance standards were unequal. Several instances of geometrical symmetry of the roles of identical twins in team competitions were noted. Twin brothers played on the right and left wings in the same soccer team, and corresponding cases were encountered in basketball, field hockey and waterpolo.

A new chapter of genetic determination—a better term might be predetermination—is currently being introduced into human biology by the fact that increasing numbers of athletes choose marriage partners from their own group. This trend is noticeable on the champion level, as in the much publicized cases of the Zatopeks, Connollys and Brightwells (Fig. 41) as well as in the world of sport and physical education in general. Because of the organizational pattern of the athletic movement there is even a trend toward "specialists"—swimmers, track and field athletes, fencers, and others—to marry among themselves. Magnitude, extent and specificity of the "genetic privileges" thus conveyed to their offspring remain to be identified by statisticians whose predictions will have to be tested by future generations of sports scientists.

P. B. Medawar distinguishes between two systems of heredity: The first he calls endosomatic (internal heredity), the second, exosomatic (external heredity). The former, which is based upon the biologically predetermined interplay of chromosomes, we have in common with other animals. The latter is particularly human, handed down from generation to generation through education and training. While enormous variants of genetic endowment for athletics are encountered in any large population group, the effectiveness of athletic training is great but limited in scope. In order to utilize the available talent, a systematic effort will have to be made in the future to ascertain on an

FIGURE 41. Of special relevance for the scientific study of the problem of the future of athletic records is the current trend among outstanding athletes to seek their marital partners within the narrow population sample to which they belong, *viz.,* that distinguished by exceptional performances in sport. Thus, a cultural characteristic of recent origin tends to become biologically permanent. The picture shows Miss D. Packer, winner of the 800-meter race in Tokyo in 1964, with her future husband R. Brightwell who won bronze and silver medals in the 400-meter single and the 4 × 400-meter relay race. Many other marriages of outstanding track and field athletes, swimmers, fencers, and others have occurred during recent years, best known among them those of the Zatopeks and the Connollys.

individual basis the genetic potential of the nation's youth for various tasks, mental as well as physical. Techniques of developing athletic performance potentials are at present applied haphazardly. Thus, we miss many, probably the majority, of the most gifted. But it is only from the latter that optimal results of training can be expected.

Infectious Diseases

Until the beginning of the last quarter of the nineteenth century, society's attitude toward epidemics was a curious mixture of erroneous theory and common sense. In the meantime major public health measures have brought the goal of total elimination of most infectious diseases on earth within reach. Epidemic diseases have been effectively controlled through vector destruction, chemotherapy, insecticides, vaccination, immunization and sanitation. Other infectious diseases were eliminated by a variety of procedures: typhoid, cholera, and dysentery by the prevention of contamination of food; plague and typhus by rat control and louse destruction; scrub typhus and venereal disease by chemotherapy; yellow fever, smallpox, diphtheria and poliomyelitis by immunization. As regards the latter disease the United States has reduced the incidence of cases from 38,476 in 1954 to 121 in 1964. These historically unique developments are reflected in an overall performance increase of the population (see Table V-C).

Of all known medical problems concerning physical fitness and also conditioning of athletes for competitions, that of protecting them from infectious diseases is by far the most important. The immunological status of each child may well determine its performance capacity. Countries with effective public health services attain the best overall athletic performance standards, and vice versa. *Physical training does not enhance resistance to infectious diseases.*

After his return to London with the British Olympic athletes from Melbourne in 1956, James Cussen (1957) reported that the most irksome troubles he had with members of the team were infections. Nasopharyngeal infections, he said, occurred frequently if the weather was cold and if there was much dust in the air. There were many cases of sore throats, nasal catarrh with closure of the Eustachian tubes and consequent deafness, as well as coughs. Skin infections were quite common. Pimples, boils, carbuncles, impetigo and tinea of the feet progressing to lymphangitis required attention. Of the latter several cases were encountered. As the weather became warmer, gnat bites were common and severe inflammatory reactions from them were troublesome.

Writing on his experience in the Olympic village in Tokyo in 1964, D. F. Hanley (1965) mentioned that several of the athletes from Ghana had chronic malaria and anemia and that their performances were therefore greatly impaired. Athletes from other African countries were similarly afflicted. Even among the highly trained U.S. athletes, intercurrent infections, particularly of the respiratory and gastrointestinal systems and of the skin, ranked as chief medical problems during their stay in Japan.

The fact that physical training fails to enhance *immunological resistance* represents one of the most important results of clinical research in athletics. It contrasts sharply with evidence to the effect that sustained exercise exerts an inhibiting influence upon the *aging process,* including several of its pathological accompaniments.

In the course of the University of Kentucky Physical Fitness Study undertaken in 1958 and 1959 at the Lexington Catholic High School, two groups of children between thirteen and fifteen years of age were examined in accordance with standardized developmental, physiological, psychological, medical, behavioral and physical performance criteria. Each group consisted of about fifty boys and fifty girls, i.e. a total of two hundred subjects were under observation. The general objective of the research was to ascertain the effect of daily intensive school physical training upon the personality structure of adolescent children. Fifty of the boys and fifty of the girls were included in the activity group, while the remainder were studied for purposes of control.

During the eighth week of the fitness experiment one of the most serious influenza epidemics that had ever been observed in Lexington, Kentucky, struck the community, unexpectedly and with great suddenness. Between February 26, 1959 and March 16, 1959, large numbers of children became afflicted. At the height of the wave almost half of the school population was absent. In our sample the normal average absentee ratio of 2.6 percent rose to an unprecedented level of between 42 and 46 percent (Fig. 42).

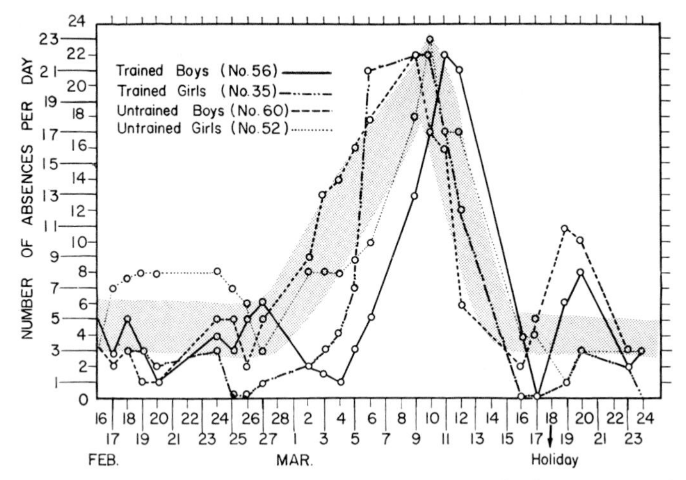

FIGURE 42. Records of absenteeism before, during and after a severe influenza epidemic which struck Lexington Catholic High School while an experiment on the effects of intensive physical training on previously sedentary adolescent boys and girls was in progress. The impact on the trained boys and girls did not differ from that on the untrained controls.

The impact of the epidemic was precisely the same upon the trained and upon the untrained children. The fact that the preceding two months of training had significantly improved the "experimental" group's physical performances, while the physical performance status of the controls remained unchanged, proved to be devoid of immunological relevance.

Not only is the trained athlete's resistance toward infections not increased, but clinical observations have shown that in the presence of infections, more particularly of infections of viral origin, strenuous exercise often exacerbates the disease process. For example, during the 1947 poliomyelitis epidemic in Great Britain, Ritchie Russell noted large numbers of persons developing the paralytic symptoms within a day following strenuous athletic or other forms of physical exertion. The probable explanation is that the virus' transmigration from the circulatory to the central nervous system is facilitated as a result of changes of permeability of the hemo-neural barrier. These changes occur as a physiological correlate of the exercise situation which proves to be of catastrophic consequence in special situations such as those under reference.

Stability of Connective Tissue

L. Prokop (In H. Groll, Leistungsgrenze in Gymnastik und Turnen, Oesterreichischer Bundesverlag fuer Unterricht, Wissenschaft and Kunst, Wien und Muenchen, 1966, p. 7 ff.) has raised the question whether limitations of athletic record performances in athletes are determined by the "vulnerability of human connective tissue." He asks whether bones, skeletal muscles and ligaments of healthy champion athletes respond to maximal use in sport and athletics with "irreversible pathological changes." The answer to Prokop's question is in the negative. It is of course true that athletic *injuries* frequently involve connective tissue. But to assume from this fact that vulnerability of connective tissue due to *physiological* usage sets a *categorical* boundary to further improvements of athletic records would amount to a logical non sequitur. In fact, the relative rarity of injuries of connective tissue structures among *top level* performers, e.g. track and field athletes and swimmers, stands in striking contrast to the high incidence of injuries of connective tissue structures among *untrained* participants in sport, impressively shown by the high accident rate among "weekend skiers." The issue therefore relates to the question of morphological and functional *adaptations to training* and to the *inverse relationship between accident proneness and motor skill.* Furthermore, many so-called sports injuries affecting connective tissue are due to factors other than the impact of kinetic forces. Sir Adolphe Abrahams has pointed out more than twenty years ago that latent unrecognized *chronic infections* are a common cause of charley horse type muscle lesions in athletes.

The majority of connective tissue injuries in athletes—other than those caused by gross trauma—are not due to *mechanical* stresses engendered during normal sport and physical education activities; nor are they due to an impairment of resistance to stress of connective tissue caused by physiological usage. Kral, Bosak and Pros (Groll, *op. cit.*, p. 54 ff) have pointed out that acute and chronic spinal column injuries in women gymnasts are invariably results of *unphysiological* demands, e.g. by acrobatic maneuvers. The latter are unacceptable not only from the medical standpoint, but they are also unsatisfactory in terms of esthetic criteria, as the 1966 World Championships in Gymnastics in Dortmund, Germany, have shown.

Summarizing, "vulnerability" toward *physiological* stresses of connective tissue cannot be considered a limiting factor for the further growth of athletic records.

Nutrition

The Food and Agriculture Organization of the United Nations has conducted global surveys of the amount of food eaten in various regions of the world. High caloric consumption levels indicate that the majority of the population receive their vital dietary requirements so that their energy expenditure need not be restricted (Table XIII).

A striking relationship appears when participation and achievement in Olympic Games are evaluated against caloric consumption levels. Nations which have little to eat are poorly represented in the Olympic contests, while participation rates and number of points gained in the various athletic events rise concomitantly with the amount of food consumed. Supporting this finding, the point level of *individual* athletes is also found to be related to the mean caloric consumption.

The 1963 Annual Report of the Food and Agriculture Organization of the United Nations indicates that existing differences in the nutritional status of the world's population will persist and possibly become more accentuated. In 1962-1963, food production per capita

TABLE XIII

OLYMPIC PARTICIPATION AND ACHIEVEMENT OF NATIONS ON DIFFERENT LEVELS OF CALORIC CONSUMPTION*

Kilocalories per Head per Day	*Population in Millions*	*Participations*	*Participation Rate*	*Point Share*	*Point Rate*	*Point Level*
1500 — 1999	432	40	0.09	610	1.4	15.3
2000 — 2499	749	397	0.53	8 709	11.6	21.9
2500 — 2999	82	264	3.24	5 936	72.7	22.5
3000 — 3499	232	969	4.17	29 324	126.1	30.3

*Tables XIII-XVII: Jokl, Karvonen Kihlberg, Koskela and Noro introduced a statistical method of assessing the major determinants of maximal athletic performances. The relevance of the new method lay in the fact that it allowed the measurement of different sport events at Olympic games on an absolute scale of evaluation. The winner in each contest is given 100 points (it being taken for granted that every gold medalist is the world's best performer in his event at the time of his victory); the competitor ranking last 0 point. The "point-distance" between the winner and the athlete placed second, third, etc., in any given competition depends on the total number of participants: the larger the number of participants, the shorter the interval. The following four statistical entities could thus be computed: Participation rate: number of participants per million inhabitants of the country; Point share: number of points collected by a country; Point rate: number of points collected per million inhabitants; Point level: average number of points per participant. The data obtained in this manner were correlated with statistical information pertaining to a variety of problems such as nutrition, death rates, infant mortality, economic and climatic conditions.

has risen by 3 percent in Western Europe and by 2 percent in North America, while in the Far East it has fallen by 1 percent and in Latin America by 2 percent. There is as yet no sign of a closing of the gap between the underdeveloped, underfed countries and the prosperous parts of the world, where overfeeding is causing obesity to become a major health problem.

Death Rates

When death rates were related to athletic achievements, it was noted that point aggregates are significantly higher for countries with rates below fifteen deaths per 1000 inhabitants, while countries with higher death rates collect significantly fewer points at Olympic Games (Table XIV). A correspondingly sliding sequence was computed for participation rates, point shares and point levels.

An analysis of death rates according to causes revealed additional information. For example, the countries standing highest in Olympic participation and success points had the highest death rates for cancer. This is, however, to be expected since a decrease in the general death rate is bound to lead to a proportional increase of individuals who live longer and are therefore more likely to be afflicted with cancer. The predominant causes of death in people under thirty years of age are the infectious diseases. In the underdeveloped countries this is the largest age group in the mortality tables.

Infant Mortality

Figures for infant mortality show a distinct relationship to athletic achievement. The countries with the highest rates of infant mortality are the ones with the lowest rates of athletic success, and vice versa. The inverse relationship between infant mortality and athletic success also becomes apparent when average point levels are plotted against

XIV

DEATH RATE AND OLYMPIC PARTICIPATION AND ACHIEVEMENT

Deaths per 1000 Inhabitants	*Population in Millions*	*Participations*	*Participation Rate*	*Point Share*	*Point Rate*	*Point Level*
5.0 — 9.9	275	902	3.28	25 962	94.4	28.8
10.0 — 14.9	460	1 493	3.25	35 667	77.6	23.9
15.0 — 19.9	389	122	0.31	1 982	5.1	16.2
20.0 — 24.9	205	212	1.03	3 708	18.0	17.5

infant mortality (Table XV). The most successful athletes come from countries with the lowest infant mortality.

Evidently the infant mortality rate is a reliable indicator of cultural and social trends which find expression also in sports and athletics. More specifically, infant mortality reflects the incidence of all illnesses to which children are subjected during the important years of their growth and development. Ratios used for measuring Olympic success are therefore most favorable in societies whose children enjoy the greatest freedom from disease, from hunger and want.

TABLE XV

INFANT MORTALITY AND OLYMPIC PARTICIPATION AND ACHIEVEMENT

Deaths per 1000 Live Births	*Population in Millions*	*Participations*	*Participation Rate*	*Point Share*	*Point Rate*	*Point Level*
25 — 49	187	688	3.68	22 011	117.7	32.0
50 — 74	160	621	3.88	15 564	97.2	25.1
75 — 99	157	580	3.69	13 428	85.5	23.2
100 — 124	90	238	2.64	5 010	55.5	21.1
125 — 149	97	415	4.28	9 405	97.0	22.7
150 — 174	386	116	0.30	1 880	4.9	16.2
175 — 199	74	172	2.32	3 351	45.3	19.5
200 — 224	18	5	0.30	74	4.0	14.8

Economic Conditions

A country's per capita income is indicative of its economic status. Table XVI correlates data for per capita income with Olympic participation and achievement ratios. The highest allocations for participation and point aggregates were obtained by countries with well-developed economies. Participation and point rates are smallest in those areas of the world in which per capita income is lowest. Point value averages are greatest for countries with high income, though there are noteworthy exceptions. It must be remembered that societies are

TABLE XVI

PER CAPITA INCOME AND OLYMPIC PARTICIPATION AND ACHIEVEMENT

Per Capita Income in Dollars	*Population in Millions*	*Participations*	*Participation Rate*	*Point Share*	*Point Rate*	*Point Level*
Less than 60	617	55	0.09	969	1.6	17.6
60 — 99	478	105	0.22	1 825	3.8	17.4
100 — 199	377	609	1.62	10 566	28.0	17.3
200 — 499	521	1 451	2.79	41 517	79.7	28.6
500 — 749	113	922	8.16	22 384	198.1	24.3
750 and over	152	194	1.28	9 016	59.4	46.5

economically stratified and that Olympic athletes invariably represent the more favorably situated strata.

Climate

The Olympic data were analyzed also to examine the question of whether rates of participation and athletic performances are determined by temperature. The accepted standard map of annual isotherm and climate zones of the world was used as the basis of evaluation. Each country was classified into temperature zones in accordance with the climatogeographic position of the region in which the majority of its population lives. Temperature zones "cold and cool," "cool and warm" and "warm and hot" include such countries in which the critical isotherms divide populated areas (Fig. 43. See also Fig. 44).

The results of the climatic analysis are summarized in Table XVII. The majority of the athletes who participate in the Olympic Games come from the three cooler zones of the world. The three warmer zones are poorly represented, *viz.*, by about only one-sixth of the total number of participants. The point rate of the warm zones amounts to only one-tenth that of the cooler countries. The 20°C. or 68°F. annual isotherm proves to be a dividing line for athletic achievement,

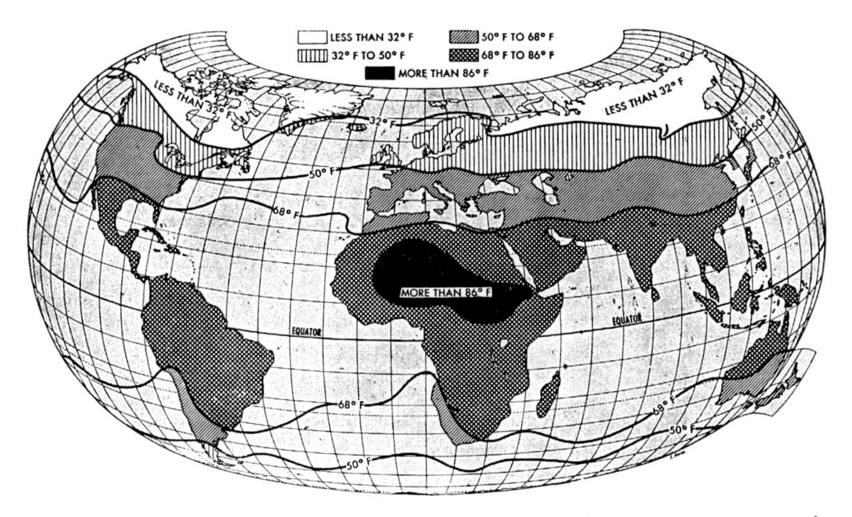

FIGURE 43. Climate: selected annual isotherms and temperature zones in the world. 32°F = 0° C, 50° F = 10°C, 68° F = 20°C, 86°F = 30°C. (Courtesy of Woytinsky and Woytinsky, 1953 p. 24.)

TABLE XVII

OLYMPIC PARTICIPATION AND ACHIEVEMENT OF THE TEMPERATURE ZONES

*Temperature Zones**	*Population in Millions*	*Participations*	*Participation Rate*	*Point Share*	*Point Rate*	*Point Level*
Cold	312	1 049	3.36	29 552	94.7	28.2
Cold & cool	246	417	1.70	14 979	60.9	35.9
Cool	401	1 395	3.48	32 472	81.0	23.3
Cool & warm	495	79	0.20	2 738	5.5	34.7
Warm	866	476	0.60	7 439	8.6	15.6
Warm & hot	64	11	0.20	146	2.3	13.3

*Annual isotherms of temperature zones:
Cold: 0° — 10°C. or 32° — 50°F.
Cool: 10° — 20°C. or 50° — 68°F.
Warm: 20° — 30°C. or 68° — 86°F.
Hot: More than 30°C. or 86°F.

though there are significant individual exceptions, due largely to the fact that technologic aids are now available to members of the affluent strata of all societies, e.g. air conditioning, which will in future exert an increasingly important influence upon the fitness of populations living in "warm" and "hot" regions.

The distinctly favorable role played by cooler climates, as shown in the Olympic analysis, raises questions of great relevance. Obviously it is not the temperature factor as such which produces a high level of physical fitness. The average untrained inhabitant of the colder countries is not *ipso facto* superior athletically. Rather, the physiologic adjustments to training take place there in a more effective manner.

The majority of mankind who reside in the hotter countries of the globe labor under a permanent handicap in that their thermoregulatory adjustments consume a great deal of their adaptation energy. A singularly important study showing the magnitude of the influence of tropical climate has been undertaken by K. S. F. Chang and coworkers (1963) who demonstrated the depressing effect of the hot summer months upon mean conception rates in Hongkong (Fig. 44). With the introduction of air conditioning of homes and of work areas, this handicap will eventually be eliminated. The technological revolution of our age of which the use of engineering devices for the control of temperatures is a part, will in due course exert a radical influence upon the physical status of the people who live in the 68 to 86°F. belt (Fig. 43). This statement also applies to the short-term effects of heat and other climatic variants upon athletic performances. The success of the first indoor standard size stadium in Houston, Texas, is largely due to the fact that it is fully air conditioned.

The shift of the main focus of civilization from Asia Minor and the Eastern Mediterranean countries to Western Europe two millennia ago followed the perfection of building techniques which allowed effective inside heating during the cold winter months. Air conditioning will likewise reduce in due course the paralyzing effects of hot climates whose debilitating influence has been taken for granted since the dawn of history.

The physiological rationale upon which this prediction is based is derived from observations to the effect that it is exposure to *unmitigated* and not to *intermittent* heat that reduces the organism's powers of adjustment. Thus, if and when working, living and sleeping climates in the hot regions of the world are controlled, the traditional impairment of human power in tropical and subtropical regions will disappear.

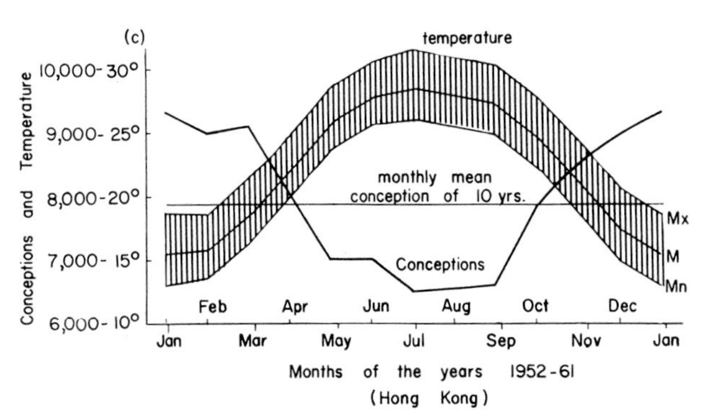

FIGURE 44. Annual fluctuations of mean conception rates and of air temperature in Hong Kong during the ten-year period 1952-1961. The "mean" conception rate for the same period is represented by the "horizontal" line. The evidence under reference represents a measurable indicator of nature and magnitude of the physiological drain imposed by climatic extremes upon adaptation energy. (Courtesy of K. S. F. Chang *et al.*, 1963.)

Altitude

Experiences with champion athletes have shown that altitudes of between 5,000 and 7,500 feet significantly influence performances in track races. They do so in a twofold manner. Contests of between 100 and 400 meters yield slightly better results than at sea level, while running times in middle and long distance races are slower. Corresponding observations are available in horse racing,* swimming,† cycling and other sports. Training and acclimatization cannot nullify the inhibiting effect of altitude upon performances of endurance, even though training at high altitude for competitions at high altitude is useful.**

Prior to 1963 no data had been presented from which magnitudes of modification of athletic performances at medium altitudes could be assessed. In 1963 we published results of a comparative analysis of competitive running and swimming time obtained at sea level and at altitudes of 5,340 and 7,347 feet.‡ Our study had been designed to test three hypotheses:

1. The lowered atmospheric pressure at high altitudes decreases all physical performances which are dependent upon *sustained* oxygen intake, while it facilitates brief efforts such as sprinting races which depend upon the incurrence of an "oxygen debt."

2. Increasing levels of oxygen lack caused by extended physical activities at different altitudes will be reflected in corresponding decreases of performances.

3. The magnitude of the effects of different altitudes will become identifiable through the evaluation of standardized sequences of progressive athletic efforts, for example, of races over distances of 100, 200, 400, 800, 1,500, 5,000, 10,000 and 42,000 meters.

The terms "oxygen debt" and "steady state" were introduced by A. V. Hill in 1925. The term "oxygen debt" expresses the deficit in oxygen intake during exercise that must be repaid after the effort. "Oxygen debt" can thus be defined as the excess oxygen consumption

---

*All present world records in horse racing over the short distances, i.e. from one-quarter mile to three and one-half furlongs were established in Mexico City where the highest standard sized race course in the world is located, while none of the records for the longer races were run on tracks situated above sea level.

†During the 'Pre-Olympic Games' in Mexico City in October 1967, Debbie Meyer won the 800 meter swimming contest in 9:48.0 min., 25.1 seconds slower than her own world mark established shortly before at sea level.

**Robert F. Grover, John H. K. Vogel and Gustav C. Voigt (*Amer J Cardiol, 18* [No. 6]: 928-932, 1966) have pointed out that "athletes suffer more from altitude than nonathletes." The ubiquitous problem of adaptation to altitude is therefore of special relevance in this context.

‡E. Jokl and P. Jokl, The Effect of Altitude on Athletic Performances. Royal Canad. Legion's Coaching Review, I, 3, 1963, 1-5. See also J. T. Reeves, P. Jokl and J. E. Cohn, Performance of Olympic Runners at Altitudes of 7,350 and 5,350 feet, Amer. Rev. Resp. Dis., 92 (No. 5), 813-816, Nov. 1965.

after the performance over and above the resting consumption of oxygen. The term "steady state" relates to a condition in which oxygen requirements and oxygen supply during the performance are balanced on a level that reflects the utilization of oxygen in the muscles. During a 100-meter race, oxygen requirements rise to an equivalent of 30 liters per minute corresponding to a release of 14.4 horsepower. But only about one-half liter of oxygen is actually burnt in the muscles so that the runner terminates the sprint with an oxygen debt of 5 liters* which is one-third of the maximum debt possible. During 400-meter races the entire oxygen debt mechanism can be utilized. The lowering of atmospheric pressure at altitudes of between 5,000 and 7,500 ft. and the impairment of oxygen intake thus caused will not detract from the running efficiency of sprinters and 400-meter runners, since their energy requirements are satisfied "anaerobically:" The oxygen debt incurred by them during the race is repaid *after* the performance. Since the density of the air at these altitudes diminishes, the runners' efforts may be actually aided as a result of the reduction of air resistance.† One liter of oxygen consumed equals about 5 kg calories. Insofar as oxygen uptake is reduced in proportion to the lowering of atmospheric pressure at higher altitudes, calorie equivalents are thus lessened with the result that all athletic performances which depend upon sustained oxygen intake are reduced.

In subjects acclimatized to altitudes of 2,400 meters or 7,500 ft., aerobic capacity is reduced by 15 percent while *pulmonary ventilation* is increased by 25 percent with the result that an incommensurately large proportion of the total oxygen intake is shunted to the musculature of the chest. The effect of altitude upon ventilation becomes even greater with acclimatization. Athletes are more susceptible to infections if they perform at higher altitudes, a fact ascribed by Astrand and co-authors (1963) to the strain on the epithelium of the respiratory track due to larger volumes of air being heated and saturated with water vapor during their passage to the alveolar spaces. Despite vaccinations and other prophylactic measures, the frequencies of in-

---

*About one-sixth of one minute's requirement level.

†Between sea level and 7,500 ft. elevation, atmospheric pressure is lowered from 762 mm Hg to 559 mm Hg. The pressure difference amounts to 27 percent, that of air density to 23 percent. Oxygen pressure of inspired air is reduced from 159 to 121, and of alveolar air from 103 to 71 mm Hg.

fections, especially of angina, was quite high among members of the Swedish team during the Olympic winter games in Squaw Valley in 1960. At the end of the sojourn at Squaw Valley, three Swedish cross country skiers whose adjustment to the altitude was studied in a series of experiments at sea level, in a low pressure chamber as well as in loco, suffered from infections of the upper air passages. Two of them had high fever.

At higher altitudes, athletes are more than usually exhausted after their races. Most of the 400-meter runners at the Pan-American Games in Mexico City in 1956 suffered from the syndrome which was described as "indisposition after running" or—because of its symptomatological similarity with "mountain sickness," "air sickness," "sea sickness"—as "athlete's sickness." As every coach knows, it is characterized by headache, nausea, vomiting and a pronounced feeling of weakness.

At the U.S. NCAA track and field championships in Albuquerque, New Mexico (elevation of 4,600 ft) on June 13 to 15, 1963, several athletes experienced signs of exhaustion such as they had not previously known. Marin, who won the three-mile race, complained about severe dizziness. During the 3,000-meter steeplechase, Pat Traynor got sick, fell into the water jump and was unable to continue. Five of the sixteen starters in the six-mile run dropped out. All the distance runners were aware of the altitude effects prior to the race and felt apprehensive.

Astrand's report of his experiences at Squaw Valley contains the following:

> Some of the cross country skiers collapsed during the competitions. Among them Per Erik Larson who has always failed in competitions at high altitudes, so also this time. In Sweden he was first or second best but now he finished as number 17 in the 15 km race, beaten by Jernberg with about 2 minutes. In the men's 4 × 10 km relay J. Stefansson collapsed after about 5 km and lost more than 3 minutes in the second half of the distance (he started as number 1, but finished as number 8). He had no infection and the test on the bicycle ergometer prior to the relay race was normal. His symptoms during and after the collapse were dizziness, headache, cold perspiration, tachycardia and he does not remember much from the later part of the race. Spectators told that Stefansson was suddenly very "old" in his behavior, got pale, stag-

gered and on a distance of about 50 meters he lost 30 seconds to the Finn and Norwegian.

In races over 1,500 meters the athlete cannot rely upon his anaerobic energy resources.* He must establish a steady state level of oxygen intake that is commensurate with his performance, except at the end of the race. During the final spurt, he always incurs an oxygen debt. Since at elevations between 5,300 ft and 7,500 ft partial oxygen pressure and therefore oxygen uptake are reduced, performances of endurance of all kinds are likely to be significantly lower, pari passu with the increase of the elevation and the extension of the distance of the races. In Mexico City in 1968, the greatest reductions in running times are to be expected in the 10,000-meter and the marathon, in swimming, over the 1,500-meter distance.

Of the last four Pan-American Games, three were held at or near sea level (Buenos Aires 1951, Chicago 1959 and Sao Paulo 1963), while one (Mexico City 1955) as well as the U.S. Pan-American trials in Boulder, Colorado, took place at elevations of 7,340 and 5,300 feet, respectively (Fig. 45). The overall performance capacity of the athletes who competed in the running events at these five meetings was sufficiently constant to be used for a comparative analysis. The competitors represented the best U.S., and in the case of the Pan-American Games, also the best Latin American runners at the time.

The superior results in all except the short track and the 100-meter swimming races at Sao Paulo in 1963 as compared with those in Buenos Aires in 1951 reflected the general performance acceleration during the years 1951-1964, while the deviation from this trend in the middle and long distance running as well as swimming times at Mexico City and Boulder are even more significant than the figures in Tables XVIII and XIX indicate. As mentioned earlier, in the past fifty years top level performances in all swimming and running events have been improved at a known rate. The magnitude of this improvement which must be taken into account in the evaluation of the data, exceeds the range of chance fluctuations of performances of individual

---

*The most remarkable athletic performance of endurance at altitude is the 3:55.0,) min. mile race run in July 1967 by Keino at Nyeri, Kenya (5.900 feet above sea level.)

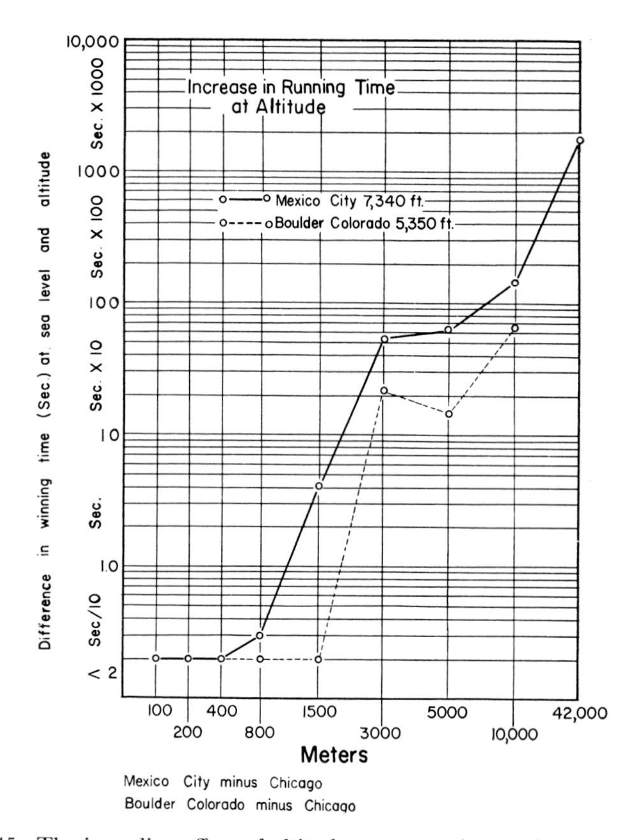

FIGURE 45. The impeding effect of altitude upon running performances is shown on logarithmic paper so as to evaluate on a common scale times in races from 100 meters to 42 km. Differences of less than .2 second have not been plotted. Thus, the significant trend towards improvement at higher elevations of the 100, 200 and 400 meter results is not shown. The handicapping influence of the lowered oxygen pressure becomes statistically valid only for distances of 1,500 meters and longer. The two ascending lines do *not* indicate running times but *differences of running times* between sea level and Boulder and Mexico City. The impairment through altitude of athletic performances of endurance cannot be nullified through training.

athletes. Figure 46 is representative of a broad pattern of performance growth which applies similarly to the other athletic contests of the "steady state" category. (For conversion of altitude measurements see Table XX.) As regards the question of adaptation, we refer to a paper by H. Reindell et al. (Bericht uber die medizinischen Versuche zur Vorbereitung auf die Olympischen Spiele 1968 in Mexico, Nat.

TABLE XVIII

WINNING TIMES, PAN-AMERICAN GAMES

Event (meters)	*Buenos Aires sea level 2/25/51*	*Mexico City 7347 ft 5/12/55*	*Chicago 598 ft 8/28/59*	*Boulder Col.* 5354 ft 6/19/59*	*Sao Paulo sea level 5/27/63*
100	10.6‡	10.3	10.3	10.5	10.3
200	21.7	20.6	20.7	20.8	21.2
400	47.8	45.4	46.1	46.1	46.7
800	1:53.2	1:49.7	1:49.4	1:47.9	1:48.3
1,500	4:00.4	3:53.2	3:49.1	3:47.5	3:43.5
3,000†	9:32.0	9:46.8	8:56.4	9:19.3	9:07.9
5,000	14:57.2	15:30.6	14:28.4	14:47.6	14:25.7
10,000	31:08.6	32:42.6	30:17.2	31:22.4	29:52.1
42,000 (marathon)	2:35:00.0	2:59:09.2	2:27:54.2	———	2:26:53.6

* National AAU meet, Pan American trials
† Steeplechase = 2 mile time
‡ times given as: hours: minutes: seconds: tenths
Data from: *United States Olympic Books,* 1952, 1956 and 1960. New York, U.S. Olympic Association; and *Track and Field News,* July, 1959.

TABLE XIX

FREE STYLE SWIMMING RACES, PAN-AMERICAN GAMES

Men	*Buenos Aires 1951*	*Mexico City 1955*	*Chicago 1959*	*Sao Paulo 1963*	*Difference between Mexico City & Chicago*
100 m	58.8	57.7	56.3	54.7	1.4
400 m	4:52.4	4:51.3	4:31.4	4:19.3	19.9
1,500 m	19:23.3	20:04.0	17:53.2	17:26.2	2:10.8
Women					
100 m	1:08.4	1:07.7	1:03.8	1:02.8	3.9
200 m	2:32.4	2:32.5	2:18.5	2:17.5	14.0
400 m	5:26.7	5:32.4	4:55.9	4:52.7	36.5

Data from: *United States Olympic Books,* 1952, 1956 and 1960.

Olymp. Komitee fur Deutschland, 1967, p. 25) reported that athletes who had flown by jet plane from Freiburg, Germany (sea level) to Mexico City responded initially to standardised exercise tests with a marked drop of blood sugar (*arterial* samples were drawn). After 2 weeks of training at Mexico City, this unusual autonomic reaction was no longer in evidence. Reindell's team also tested a second group of athletes who prior to their flight to Mexico City had undergone a 10 day period of preparatory training at Fort Romeu in France at an elevation of just under 6,000 feet. The initial hypoglycemic response to the standardised exercise tests was distinctly less marked in the latter as against the Freiburg group. Also, the adjustment of blood sugar regulation appeared to be better and quicker in the Ford Rameu athletes.

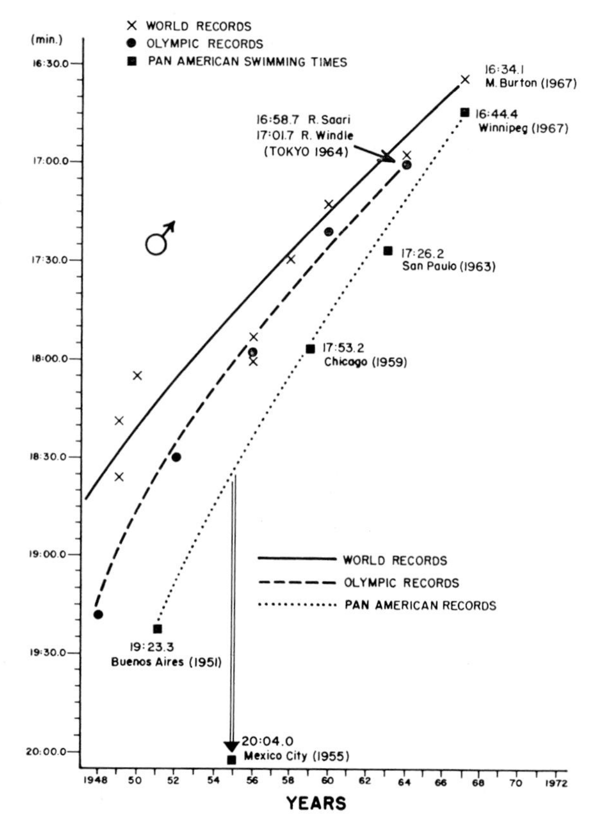

FIGURE 46. In order to arrive at a comparative evaluation of athletic performances that lie several years apart, attention must be paid to the growth of athletic records that has taken place during the past decades. The ascending curves for world, Olympic, and other records established under standardized conditions ascend, each in a pattern of its own. Because of the constancy of the trends under reference it is possible to assess the "relative value" of past and present results as well as to predict—within known limits—future achievements. Figure 46 depicts the evolution of 1,500-meter free style swimming performances for men between 1948 and 1967. In 1963 we computed growth curves of world and Olympic records and "extrapolated" them until 1967. The probability that the winner in Tokyo in 1964 would reach a time within one standard deviation from the dotted line was stated to be 96 percent. Robert Windle of Australia won the gold medal in 17:01.7, thus corroborating the validity of the prediction. Similarly, M. Burton's 1967 world record of 16:34.1 is precisely in accordance with the statistically assessed projection.

The dotted curve indicates the performance growth of the winning times at the Pan American Games. The magnitude of the handicapping influence of the altitude of Mexico City upon the endurance event is evident from the result attained by the victor in 1955.

TABLE XX-A

CONVERSION TABLE

Meters	*Feet*	*Meters*	*Feet*
1	3.28	3,500	11,480
500	1,640	4,000	13,120
1,000	3,280	4,500	14,760
1,500	4,920	5,000	16,400
2,000	6,560	5,500	18,040
2,500	8,200	6,000	19,680
3,000	9,840		

TABLE XX-B

Best Altitude Performances in Track Events to Date, Listed for Elevations Below and Above 5000 Feet

	2500-5000-Feet		*5000-Plus Feet*	
400m			45.4	Lou Jones (US) Mexico City '55 (7350)
440	45.8	Daniel Rudisha (Ken) Kisumu '67 (3730)	45.8	Ulis Williams (US) Albuquerque '63 (5100)
880	1:46.3	Wilson Kiprugut (Ken) Kisumu '67 (3730)	1:47.2	Jim Ryun (US) Albuquerque '67 (5100)
1500m	3:38.1	Kip Keino (Ken) Lusaka '67 (4500)	3:46.4	Bodo Tummler (WG) Mexico City '67 (7350)
Mile	3:53.1	Kip Keino (Ken) Kisumu '67 (3730)	3:58.7	Kip Keino (Ken) Nyeri '67 (5900)
2Mile	9:01.0	Terry Sullivan (Rho) Salisbury '63 (4780)	8:50.4i	George Scott (Aus) Albuquerque '67 (5300)
3Mile	13:31.6	Kip Keino (Ken) Kisumu '67 (3730)	13:33.8	Naftali Temu (Ken) Nairobi '67 (5450)
5000m	13:53.6	Leonid Ivanov (USSR) Alma-Ata '65 (2950)	14:20.0	Alvaro Mejia (Col) Mexico City '66 (7350)
6Mile	28:28.2	Andrew Arap Soi (Ken) Kisumu '64 (3730)	28:16.4	Naftali Temu (Ken) Nairobi '67 (5450)
10,000m	28:53.8	Leonid Ivanov (USSR) Alma-Ata '65 (2950)	30:10.8	Alvaro Mejia (Col) Mexico City '66 (7350)
3000mSt	8:41.4	Viktor Kudinsky (USSR) Alma-Ata '65 (2950)	8:57.8	Gaston Roelants (Bel) Mexico City '67 (7350)
Marathon	2:25:48.2	Kanda (Rho) Bulawayo '64 (4215)	2:19:37.0	Gaston Roelants (Bel) Mexico City '67 (7350)
440IH	49.3	Gert Potgieter (SA) Bloemfontein '60 (4310)	49.6	Rex Cawley (US) Albuquerque '63 (5100)
MileR	3:06.8	Iowa Provo '67 (4530)	3:05.2	Iowa Albuquerque '67 (5100)

TABLE XX-C

Cities Where Track and Field Meetings Are Being Held Regularly at Altitudes Between 2950 and 8660 Feet Above Sea Level

Addis-Ababa, Ethiopia	7750	Kisumu, Kenya	3730
Alamosa, Colorado	7545	South Lake Tahoe, California	7350
Albuquerque, New Mexico	5100	Los Alamos, New Mexico	7330
Alma-Ata, USSR	2950	Lusaka, Zambia	4500
Aspen, Colorado	7930	Lyeninakan, USSR	5280
Bloemfontein, South Africa	4310	Laramie, Wyoming	7300
Bogota, Columbia	8660	Malopi, South Africa	6000
Boulder, Colorado	5350	Mexico City, Mexico	7350
Bulawayo, Rhodesia	4215	Nairobi, Kenya	6450
Cheyenne, Wyoming	6135	Nyeri, Kenya	5900
Colorado Springs, Colorado	5980	Ogden, Utah	4310
Denver, Colorado	5280	Patchefstroom, South Africa	5365
El Paso, Texas	4200	Pretoria, South Africa	4470
Flagstaff, Arizona	6890	Provo, Utah	4530
Font-Romeu, France	6820	Reno, Nevada	4380
Germiston, South Africa	5480	Salisbury, Rhodesia	4780
Johannesburg, South Africa	5690	Salt Lake City, Utah	4390
Kampala, Uganda	3730	Santa Fe, New Mexico	6950

(Courtesy Tom Gleason and Jack Shephard: *Track and Field News*, Los Altos, Calif.)

Chapter VI

PATTERN FORMATION

To reiterate, there is in all athletic record performances a qualitative element which defies scientific measurement. As in the fine arts, in literature and music, every champion athlete evolves superior performance techniques of his own. The African Watusi used a "modern" high jumping style centuries before it was introduced at the Olympic Games. Originality of pattern formation decisively contributed to the Olympic successes in the hammer throw by Harold Connolly, who is afflicted with combined upper and lower plexus paralyses of the left brachial plexus; by Karoly Takacs who, having participated in the pistol-shooting competition at the 1936 Olympic games, lost his dominant right arm in an accident but returned to London in 1948 to win a gold medal in this event, using his left arm; and by Lis Hartel, who in Helsinki in 1952 and in Stockholm in 1956 proved to be the greatest equestrienne of her time, notwithstanding the fact that she suffered from extensive quadripareses of poliomelitic origin.

Insofar as increments of physical performances depend upon improvements of man's environment, their range is finite. Bakwin and McLaughlin (1964) have presented evidence showing that the secular increase in height of boys coming from affluent strata of American society has reached its limits. We can, in fact, extrapolate human performance growth curves of various kinds, relate them to nutritional, epidemiological and other determinants, and thus arrive at reliable predictive forecasts of the effects of social and economic changes currently in progress in a given population. On the other hand, the capacity of man's brain to engender new motor patterns is unlimited. The motor act of man reflects his infinite creative potentialities. This statement does not apply to all human movements, but it applies universally to those which, in Sherrington's words, have "accompaniment of mind." In its measurable aspects as well as in respect to its communicative implications, the study of increments in physical performance therefore touches upon one of the most fascinating problems not only of physiology and clinical medicine, but also of anthropology in its entirety.

The Acquisition of Skill

Man is capable of two kinds of motor acts: movements whose structural patterns form part of the genetically determined building plan of his central nervous system; and movements which originate as mentally conceived objectives which the neuromuscular system is capable of transforming into kinetic events. Standing and walking are representative of the former; the use of tools, writing, playing musical instruments, or competing in a 110-meter hurdles race of the latter.

Not only can human beings carry out movements in the image of their thinking, but they can also improve upon their execution. The scope of this improvement ranges from a child's drawings to Michelangelo's paintings in the Sistine Chapel; from a beginner's renderings on the piano to a concert presentation by Arthur Rubinstein; from a schoolboy's efforts at the carpenter's bench to the building of wooden churches in Northern Finland; and from a young track and field contestant's performances to the point aggregates obtained by Olympic decathlon finalists.

Nature and appearance of a given motor task are mediated first through our sense organs. It is only secondarily that we become acquainted with the inherent properties of tools, implements, and other material elements involved in motor learning—the buoyancy of the water in which we swim, the expansion of the space in which we run or jump, the resistance of the snow on which we move on skis, the elastic properties of the ball which we bounce, of the wind which swells the sails of our boat. Such new categories of cognition as are thus revealed engender new motor responses in a continuous *Gestaltkreis.*

Watching and thinking do not suffice for the acquisition of skills, for learning how to ride a bicycle, how to handle a galloping horse, how to skate on ice, how to play tennis. It is through sustained practice alone that the required coordinative potentialities are developed and new cognitive qualities conveyed. The individual thereby gains decisive knowledge of "So can I do it," of keeping his balance on the bicycle, of remaining in control of the horse, of skating on ice, of swimming through a river. In other words, the initial "gnostic" approach to the acquisition of skill is supplemented by "pathic" experience. The process thus engendered of "building-up" increasingly more differentiated postural and spatial schemata of the body, at rest and in action, involves correspondingly more differentiated associations with corporeal awareness, imagery, memory, as well as three dimensional and temporal discrimination. Summation of new sense data reaching the central nervous system leads to new perceptive and cognitive integration and in turn to new and progressively more effective motor responses. Denny-Brown has referred to this adaptive process as "morphosynthesis," a neurophysiological term which relates to specific potentialities of the parietal lobes of man. It is thus—and only thus—that design and construction of "new" motor acts can be effected.

The Parietal Lobes

The acquisition of skill is invariably a protracted process. A given individual's motor capacities are not fully recognizable in the untrained state. This fact is of fundamental importance in education, in the arts and in athletics, in physiology, psychology, and very much so in neurology and psychiatry. In the latter branch of clinical medicine, the relevance of much of the voluminous literature concerning the symptomatology of lesions of the parietal lobes, of the aphasias, apraxias, agnosias, alexias, agraphias, acalculias, of tactile and visual dysfunctions, of the Gerstmann syndrome and of disorders of the body image is limited by the fact that the respective performance variants have so far not been systematically investigated in healthy subjects. As long as range and quality of skill in normal people are not identified, the elaborately constructed pyramid of clinical theories pertaining to the sector under reference rests on insecure foundations.

Macdonald Critchley's statement that "the ordinary routine neurological examination as well as conventional psychological testing fail to do justice to the nature of parietal disorders" alludes to this shortcoming. To illustrate it is appropriate to mention that clumsy young boys and girls who do poorly in their arithmetic lessons and who have difficulties in distinguishing right from left* are not infrequently "discovered" by alert physical training instructors who of course are unlikely to interpret such observations as indicative of the presence of a "congenital type of Gerstmann Syndrome"—all the more so since the above "symptoms" are apt to disappear after a few months of intensive training in the gymnasium, the swimming pool and on the playing field.

It would be unjustifiable to conclude that the parietal lobes alone are involved in the long-term adaptive responses under consideration. But the fact that disturbances of body image, of topographic memorizing, and of orientation are of specific diagnostic relevance in patients with lesions of the parietal lobes indicates that the latter are "nodal points" for all central nervous adjustments upon which the acquisition of skill depends.

von Gebsattel has pointed out that clinical analyses of the kind referred to above yield what he calls an "anti-eidos," made up from mirror images, as it were, of the norm, and that quite generally interpretation of performance anomalies observed in patients with cerebral disorders allows the elaboration of a neuropsychiatrically derived "holistic" concept of normal human behavior.

Every voluntary activity productive of patterned work can be analyzed in four stages: first, in respect of the *idea of the work* to be performed; second, with a view to the *design of the work* as imagined at the moment when the activity begins; third, in terms of the fact that a *constructive plan* must encompass the partial activities leading in appropriate sequence to the completion of the task; and fourth, with regard to the motor *technique* employed for the attainment of the objective.

Hughlings Jackson

All four components are involved in the acquisition of skill even though there is ordinarily no awareness on the part of the individual of such a design. However, the validity of the concept can be demon-

*Editorial: Clumsy Children. *Lancet,* 1252, June 8, 1963. Gubby, S. S., Ellis, E., Walton, J. N., and Court, S. D. M.: Clumsy Children: A Study of Apraxic and Agnosic Defects in Twenty-one Children. *Brain,* 88: (II) 295-312, 1965.

禁煙
NO SMOKING

strated along two lines. First by a study of patients with lesions of the parietal lobes who present a syndrome called "constructional apraxia." Secondly, by observations of extraordinarily able and determined individuals who acquire *exceptional skills* irrespective of the fact that they are afflicted with major bodily handicaps. Such a division is in accordance with Hughlings Jackson's twofold approach to neurological symptomatology, *viz.* with his categorical distinction between clinical manifestations of "destroying" and "discharging" cerebral disorders.* I consider it appropriate in the context of the present study to extend Jackson's concepts to the interpretation of neuromotor performances in their entirety, including their vast range of effectiveness and differentiation in normal subjects. In studying acquired skills we thus place in juxtaposition analyses of *performance defects* encountered in patients with lesions of the parietal lobes, and evaluations of *exceptional performance achievements* by subjects who are afflicted with anomalies of their bodily machinery of execution. If we look upon the sequelae of destructive lesions as revealing facets of the "anti-eidos" of the norm, the case histories of "handicapped" champion athletes serve to indicate points, as it were, which lie close to the outermost boundaries of the field of operation of the human

*The following quotations are from Jackson's *Selected Writings,* in 2 volumes, N.Y., Basic Books, 1958:

"Cases of paralysis and convulsions may be looked upon as the results of experiments made by disease on particular parts of the nervous system of man. The study of palsies and convulsions from this point of view is the study of the effects of 'destroying lesions' and of the effects of 'discharging lesions'." (Localisation of movements, vol. I, p. 63.).

"Abnormalities of function are of two kinds, minus and plus. In cases of hemiplegia from breaking-up of the internal capsule by clot or softening, there is destruction of fibres and also, of course, loss of function . . . while a 'discharging lesion' is an hyper-physiological condition." (Hypertonicity in paralysis, vol. II, pp. 472-473.)

"The 'discharging lesion' is an hyper-physiological 'condition' . . . and a fit of epilepsy an excessive caricature of the normal physiological process during what is called a voluntary action." (Some implications of dissolution of the nervous system, vol. II, pp. 39 and 43.)

FIGURE 47. Scene from gymnastic contests for women during the Olympic games in Tokyo in 1964. The finalists represented a highly selected group distinguished by conspicuously high natural endowment as well as by exceptional personality characteristics reflected in the sense of purpose which motivated them over long years of conscientious training.

organism's capacity to transform ideomotor concepts into action. The field within these boundaries delineates the scope of the acquisition of skill (Fig. 47).

Constructional Apraxia

Constructional apraxia (Fig. 48) occurs commonly in parietal disease. It rarely prompts the patient to make specific complaints of its existence. Kleist defined the condition as a disturbance of the ability to carry out tasks demanding spatial arrangements. Essentially, it is an executive defect within the visuospatial domain—its presence can be demonstrated by tests in which the patient is asked to copy designs made by the examiner. Most patients who perform inadequately in these tests show little dissatisfaction with their efforts. They are not or not fully aware of having failed, e.g. a housewife who can no longer lay a table for a meal, an experienced dressmaker who begins to have trouble in cutting out material from a pattern, a previously competent typist who lately encountered difficulties in writing, omitted letters and words, spelled incorrectly and used faulty grammar.

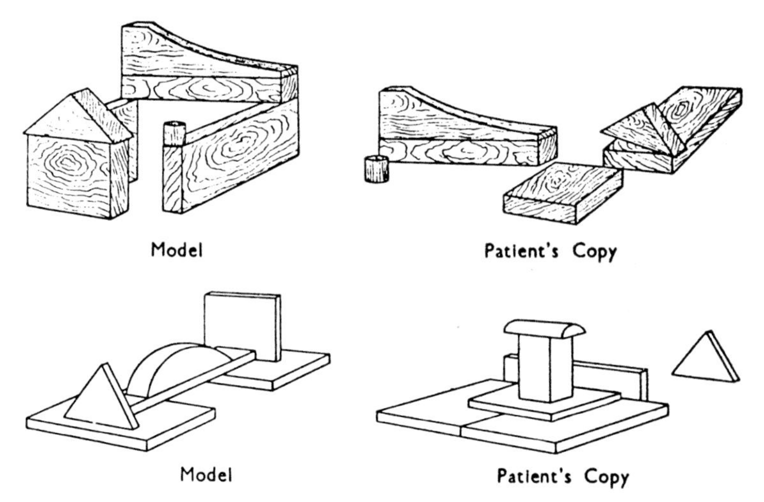

FIGURE 48. Three-dimensional constructional tasks. Patient with left fronto-parietal metastatic tumor (*A*). Three-dimensional constructional tasks. (The patient was given the appropriate bricks, but he helped himself to two others as well.) Patient with right temporoparietal glioblastoma (*B*). (Courtesy Macdonald Critchley.)

Mayer-Gross believed that constructional apraxia is an expression of "space-impairment" and that the disturbance under reference includes features of a perceptive as well as of an executive character. It is a sort of visual agnosopraxia, a deficiency not only of cognition but also of action. The condition is related to a syndrome described by Gerstmann in 1924, *viz.* of inability of patients afflicted with parietal lobe lesions to recognize their own fingers, to name them, and to point out individual digits when so directed. Macdonald Critchley has reported the case of a woman with a biparietal lesion who had for years worked as a fish filleter. With the development of her symptoms, she began to experience difficulty in carrying on with her job. She did not seem to know what to do with her knife, would stick the point in the head of a fish, start the first stroke and then come to a stop. In her own mind, she knew how to fillet fish, but yet she could not execute the maneuvre. The foreman accused her of being drunk and sent her home for mutilating fish.

Johannes Lange pointed out that the hand plays the part of a tool which connects our "personal space" with the "space around us." The same statement can of course be made in respect of the sensory and proprioceptive attributes as well as the motor potentialities of the human body as a whole even though it applies most demonstrably to the hands. The conclusion to be drawn from observations of this kind is that the acquisition of skill implies the establishment of new levels of relations between personal and extrapersonal space, an accomplishment the effectiveness of which presupposes functional integrity of the parietal lobes.

Hughlings Jackson's concept of "discharging" lesions was derived from observations of patients with epileptic seizures. However, the problem of motor discharges also applies to the initiation of "normal" movements. Its study belongs to neurophysiology as a whole and not exclusively to pathology. It involves the broad problem of the transformation of ideomotor patterns into skilled movements. The fact that many handicapped individuals, because they were unable to adopt the customary techniques of execution of standardized athletic tasks, have attained extraordinary performances by means of quite unusual and original coordinative approaches, throws new light upon the theory of the acquisition of skill.

Jean Fernel on the "Theater of the Event" and the "Event Itself"

As regards the *idea of the work to be performed,* the sixteenth century French physiologist Jean Fernel wrote, "What geography is to history, such is anatomy to medicine. Both represent theatres of events." Likewise, the acquisition of skill is a prerequisite for the execution of a large variety of purposive tasks, and with them of the communication of mind and the creation of esthetic values. Inherently, objectives are concepts that defy measurement. This consideration belongs to the realm of psychology and philosophy, of phenomenology and anthropology in its widest sense.

The evolution of objectives always precedes the evolution of motor patterns, with exceptionally gifted individuals acting as pathfinders. This statement applies to the crafts, to technology, to the arts as well as to sport. This is shown by the existence in every sphere of human interest of "schools" whose didactic techniques aiming at the cultivation of specific skills rest upon the examples set by outstanding leaders.

Selected references to the history of sport and physical training will illustrate. Prior to the second half of the eighteenth century the attainment of maximal physical performances was a matter of little concern. The summits of the Swiss Alps did not challenge the inhabitants of the valleys to climb them. When in 1787 Saussure conquered the Mont Blanc, his achievement motivated many people to acquaint themselves with the techniques of mountaineering. At the same time the desire to explore plains and rivers and forests everywhere in the world received a powerful stimulus. Such skills as were needed for the implementation of these desires were perfected. Around the end of the eighteenth century, the German naturalist, Alexander von Humboldt, undertook expeditions to the Northern and Southern hemisphere of the American continent and he described in detail what he had seen. Among those who were stimulated by his writings was Charles Darwin.

E. D. Adrian on Sensory Perception

The problem of *design of a skilled movement* cannot be divorced from that of its notation and of the methods employed to transform the mental image thus engendered into corresponding executive motor acts, a process of which E. D. Adrian has said that "the nervous system reacts to relations between stimuli and performs the appropriate task with any part of the motor system that is available. We cannot represent it as a series of machines for operating on the map of events unless we add a number of devices to make good this fundamental difference. On the sensory side there must be something to abstract the significant elements of a pattern and on the motor side something to do just the reverse, to convert the abstraction into a concrete movement." In other words, the central nervous system of man "decodes" efferent and "codes" afferent streams of impulses of the kind involved in the initiation and control of motor acts.

The Musical Study

An area in which didactic techniques designed to establish skill of execution are very far advanced is keyboard music. As an example I refer to the role of the "study" or the étude, defined in Grove's *Dictionary of Music and Musicians* as a "class of musical composition of extremely varied scope and design, whose chief object is the cultivation of the powers of execution."

Facility to play on the keyboard is achieved by practicing technical exercises, such as scales and arpeggios, by each hand separately, and consequently by both hands in unison. Up to the middle of the eighteenth century such technical exercises were taught in a dry and unattractive form. In Voltaire's *Candide*, published in 1759, the "Illustrissimo Lord Procócurante" complained that "music nowadays is merely the art of executing difficulties and in the end that which is only difficult ceases to please. Decisive attempts to improve this kind of shortcoming were made by Domenico Scarlatti and by Johann Sebastian Bach whose *Notenbüchlein* for his wife Maria Magdalena and his son Friedemann have ever since been used by music teachers. Moreover, Bach in seeking to establish the perfect relationship of the tempered scales, produced forty-eight preludes and fugues that besides being inherently beautiful, have remained the classical touchstone of piano pedagogy. More than a century later Chopin who always limbered up for his own concerts by playing from Bach's *Well-Tempered Clavichord,* presented in his twenty-four études a series of "field maps of the territory he felt had to be explored in order to enlarge the range of piano technique" (W. Brockway and H. Weinstock, *Men of Music,* New York, 1937). In almost every one of them he dealt with technical problems involved in the new kind of music he was composing. Each étude was designed as an exercise to overcome specific difficulties of execution. The study in thirds (Opus 25, No. 6) and the tremendous one in octaves (Opus 25, No. 10) reveal their teaching purposes at a glance. Even such a passionate outburst as the "revolutionary" étude (Opus 10, No. 12) is essentially a technical study of the very highest order for the left hand.

These études initiated a world-wide advancement of piano technique, as one hundred fifty years before Chopin, Bach has caused an advancement of musical technique in its entirety. The cellist Pablo Casals said that he plays Bach "so as pianists play Chopin." In setting forth technical problems, both Bach and Chopin created music of great esthetic value, thus providing the motivation without which nobody can be induced to spend the necessary time practicing. The best of Chopin's études are among the finest compositions for the piano. It has been truly said that he who can play Chopin's études can play anything in modern piano literature.

The history of the musical study represents a model of methodology for the teaching of advanced skills of all kinds. The time will come when it will serve as a didactic guide for the development of gymnastics and physical training.

Empirical Observation and Scientific Discoveries

At all times new physical skills were used in the pursuit of new human adventures following in the wake of new scientific discoveries. Balloon ascents staged in France during the second half of the nineteenth century marked the beginnings of the conquest of space. The flight in 1875 by Tissandier, Croce-Spinelli and Sivel of the "Zenith," fired the imagination of the people of Europe in a manner comparable to the excitement caused by the orbiting of the Russian "Sputnik" in 1956. During the same period, competitive athletics and swimming became popular. Performances in running, jumping, throwing, and so forth were measured, recorded and compared. A new view of scope and nature of human powers were thus engendered. In 1872 Captain Webb swam the British Channel from Dover to Calais in twenty-one hours. Evidently the scope of man's motor aptitude, strength, and endurance was wider than had so far been assumed. Modern science further aided the effectiveness of human skill. The growth of agricultural chemistry led to major improvements of food production. The infectious diseases were brought under control. People became bigger and stronger and maturated earlier. The length of life increased. Methods of physical training were evaluated in research laboratories, first in England, Germany, France, and Italy, later in other countries. Orthopedic surgeons and cardiologists became interested in the application of exercise therapy in the management of a variety of diseases. The idea of rehabilitating chronically disabled individuals was born.

As shown earlier in this monograph standards of human performances in sports and athletics have increased incessantly. The traditional assumption of a categorical inferiority of women had to be revised: Many girl swimmers now return better times than those of the world's best male performers a few decades ago. Young boys and girls today successfully aspire to performance goals beyond imagination fifty years ago. Evidently, the acquisition of human skill presupposes not only physical powers but also the realization of distinct aims and objectives. The latter in turn are conceived in the image of historical, social, cultural, and scientific precedents.

Industriousness as Prerequisite of Skill

Constructive plans for all human pursuits that aspire to the attainment of excellence of motor performance demand that the pupil spends a great *amount of time* practicing. Track champions devote four to five hours per day to their training. In their comprehensive study of Sweden's best girl swimmers, Astrand *et al.* found that performances differed in accordance with the volume of training (p. 41).

Eighty years ago John Ruskin, the British art critic, made a statement whose validity extends beyond the field to which it was meant to apply:

> If we were to be asked abruptly, and required to answer briefly, what qualities chiefly distinguished great artists from feeble artists, we should answer, I suppose, first, their sensibility and tenderness; secondly, their imagination; and thirdly, their industry. Some of us

> might, perhaps, doubt the justice of attaching so much importance to this last character, because we have all known clever men who were indolent, and dull men who were industrious. But though you may have known clever men who were indolent, you never knew a "great" man who was so; and, during such investigation as I have been able to give to the lives of the artists whose works are in all points noblest, no fact ever looms so large upon me—no law remains so steadfast in the universality of its application—as the fact and law that they are all great workers. Nothing concerning all great workers is a matter of more astonishment than the quantity they have accomplished in the given length of their life; and when I hear a young man spoken of, as giving promise of high genius, the first question I ask about him is always—Does he work?

Ruskin's law is equally valid in respect of the acquisition of skill. Its significance is greater than that of any other determinant of performance. In statistical parlance one would say that sustained practice is a determinant of the first order whose effectiveness is aided by a variety of determinants of second, third and so forth order, each of them related to the objective under reference.

The personal history of every champion athlete reveals the determining role played in his career by intensive, sustained training. Intensive, sustained training is an indispensable prerequisite for athletic as well as artistic success. Without it the full potentialities of neuromotor skill cannot unfold themselves.

Concerning the *technique* to be adopted for the establishment of acquired skills of high order, we like to quote from an account given by Eva Bosakova, the Czechoslovakian athlete, of the years of preparation which preceded her Olympic victories in the gymnastic contest on the balancing beam in 1956 and 1960. When Miss Bosakova was fifteen years old her father, himself an outstanding gymnast, began to supervise her training:

> He prescribed daily thirty-minutes periods of work on the beam during which it was necessary to remain on the appartus constantly in action, walking, hopping, turning, and again walking without rest. I spent hundreds of hours and uncounted kilometers walking and running on the beam.

After some time the beam became her favorite gymnastic event.

> I constantly searched for new methods, elements, and dynamic combinations for my exercises. In the process I gained complete confidence,

accustomed myself to unfamiliar movements and lost all fear of falling. Each individual exercise period lasted more than one hour. During this time I went through my whole routine five to seven times. Afterwards I worked on individual elements of the exercises and their connections, selected passages and their combinations. At the height of my career, it took me from about six to eight months to acquire mastery of a new exercise such as those prescribed for Olympic Games.

It is thus that skill is acquired. Sustained practice of precisely designed sequences of movements establishes advanced levels of control, of differentiation, and of precision of motor acts such as are beyond the integrative control of the untrained.

Erwin Straus on Memory

The *constructive plan* for the execution of a skilled movement also presupposes memory for its structure as well as for the components from which it is synthesized.

Straus has shown that memory is selective. Of our daily actions we generally do not retain detail but remember only "the whole" and "the remarkable." To register, Straus says, means to disengage and to arrest the fleeting from the continuum of confrontations with the world. If an event is to be remembered, it must be different and separable from other things. It has to have "marks of distinction," marks which the observer can identify. Yet, not each and every difference makes an event remarkable. There must be a significant change in the flow of events. Straus' thesis is that only the new, or the *Novum,* can be disengaged, arrested, registered and recalled. This statement applies t ideas, concepts, emotional experiences as well as to motor performances.

The *Novum* cannot be measured. It represents a specifically human happening of "historical dimensions." As to the memorability of *motor* events, only "focal acts" can thus be "disengaged." The term "focal act" was coined by Sherrington who distinguished between "grades of acts." We think, he wrote, of ourselves as engaged from moment to moment in doing this or that. This is a convenience of speech. At any given time there is but one "focal doing" which presents the keypiece of the performance to which all other motor events are subordinate. The crack pistol shot can hit his target whether he stands, sits, or lies. Postures and movements that are but contributory to the focal act are called "satellite movements." Satellite movements fit into the total pattern of the act—but they do not enter the field of awareness. Only to the "focal act" can awareness be attached and if so to but one act at a time. No individual is ever the seat of two focal acts at once, nor can two events be simultaneously recorded as memory traces. Both the main act of the moment and the memory trace thus enjoy a special position.

> The main act seems to each of us, amid a natural world which we do not control, a happening which we do control. It seems to me I do it not at the dictation of the inevitable. In turning to it I do not seem to myself to be merely carrying out something already completely fixed for me by the past. I am restricted to one such act at a time, for it is always an act which demands my fully integrated self. I cannot therefore break away from a deterministic world in several directions at once. As to the one main act which I am allowed it seems to me I have freedom of choice. (Sherrington)

Terms like "the main act" or "freedom of choice" have different connotations in different stages of the process of acquisition of skill. Even though the objectives of all differentiated motor performances are specific, their execution cannot be so in the beginning. For instance, in sport as well as in the arts a long period of conditioning and practice precedes the attainment of mastery of the task. Success or failure is eventually assessed in accordance with technical as well as interpretive criteria. The development of music into a cultural pursuit of the highest order is largely due to the fact that its content has been rendered identifiable with remarkable precision through the elaboration of staff notation. An artist's ability to perform a particular composition from staff notation is a hallmark of his competency, even though it is true that there are also other critical aspects of his performance. At the height of their concert careers some of the greatest pianists of this century, among them Busoni and Gieseking, could memorize a composition simply by looking at the score sheet, and play it without preceding practice on the keyboard. In 1961, Oxford University Press published a textbook by the viola virtuoso William Primrose under the meaningful title *Technique Is Memory*. It deals with "the relationship between memory, concentration and accuracy, and the topography of the fingerboard."

Notation of Movements

As a result of the perfection of staff notation, the student of music today has access to the collective technical and esthetic experiences of the past. He can acquaint himself with and memorize them. The athlete cannot to the same extent benefit from the skill and knowledge gained by others. However, the progressive improvement during the past decades of all performances in sport is in part due to the advancement of techniques of what Medawar calls "extrasomatic hereditary communication," through techniques which conceptualize and record acquired information and render it accessible to every beginner. Attempts to elaborate a system of staff notation of movements in physical education, sport and athletics have not yet yielded results that are comparable to those which in the past two and a half centuries have led to such remarkable developments in communication of music. Promising efforts in the graphic representation of motor performances have been made in choreography as well as in the transcription of the modern dance, of gymnastics and of calisthenics. Such universal memory traces as are avaliable, do serve every athlete as guides during his training, e.g. through coaching books, teaching charts and descriptive illustrations. While in its present form the effectiveness of such material is still limited, it is nevertheless of considerable didactic value (Fig. 49).

All acquired skills are characterized by "accompaniment of mind." In the initial stages of practicing a new task, awareness is concentrated on mechanical aspects of the act. With increasing skill, the motor event becomes progressively more automatic and the mind now concerns itself primarily with its aims and objectives. This statement applies to school physical training (Fig. 50), to competitive athletics in its many facets and, most impressively, to all artistic endeavors. On the highest levels of perfection, performance and performer seem to merge in the attainment of the objective and with it of experiences mediated by the conversion of the original ideomotor image into its execution. Man's capacity of transforming the former into the latter represents the physiological basis of all artistic pursuits in that technical mastery is the prerequisite for the creation of esthetic and emotional values. In Johann Sebastian Bach's *B-Minor Mass,* ritual, text and music combine to convey the idea of the transubstantiation of the

FIGURE 49A. Forty-five symbols representing a corresponding number of exercise units used in a longitudinal study by Jokl, Ball and Frankel in which the effect of sustained physical training on resting blood pressure of normo- and hypertensive subjects of between thirty-two and seventy-two years of age was assessed. The forty-five exercise units were detailed in a 'key-chart.'

bread and of the wine. The Greek drama demonstrates the transforming power of "catharsis," of the reverberation in the mind of the onlooker of the happenings on the stage and of their human implications. In lyrical poetry, literary allegory tells of reality undergoing a magic change: In Heinrich Heine's *Dichterliebe* tears turn into flowers and sighs into a chorus of nightingales. Corresponding categories of transformation are inherent accompaniments of the acquisition of all skills. The significance of the superb feats of the three handicapped champions to whom reference was made earlier cannot be fathomed in their entirety in terms of the athletic success attained by them; their triumphs actually altered their entire lives (p. 118).

Analyses of the above kind place into focus a theme of which the science of sport has so far taken little if any cognizance, namely that of the "value" of fitness. All concern with man's power and efficiency remains worthless unless consideration is given to the ends toward which these attributes are applied. In other words, the issue is primarily of "humanistic" and only secondarily of "scientific" relevance. A good man who is weak is preferable to a bad man who is strong.

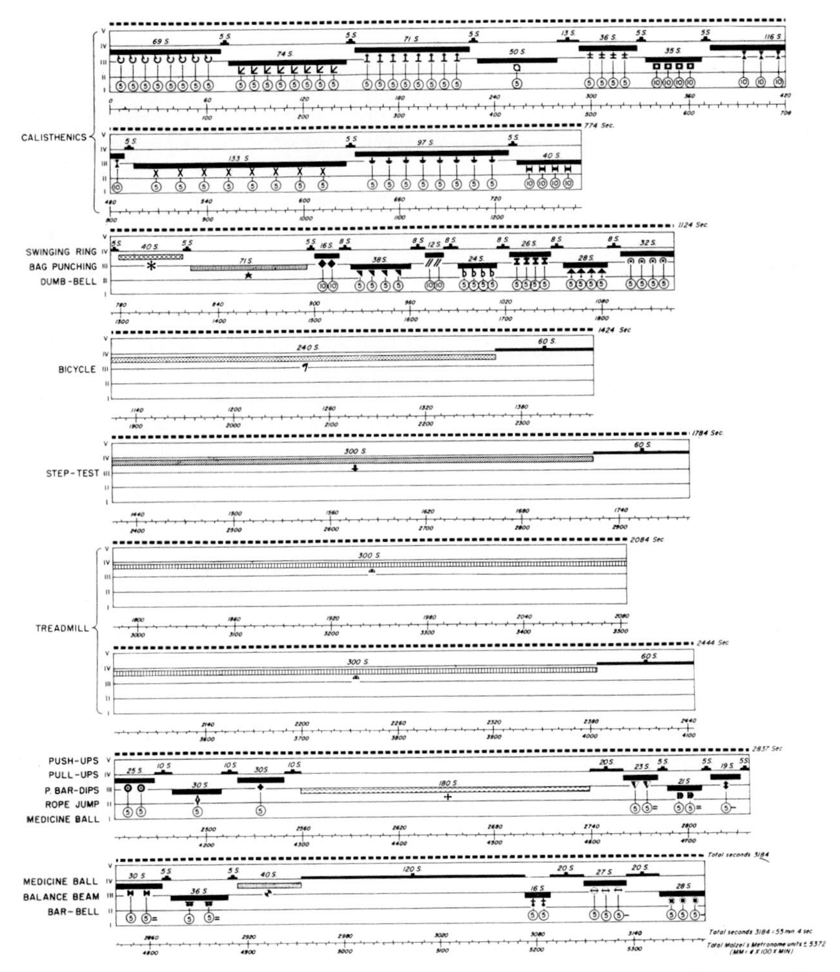

FIGURE 49B. Sample of one-page sheet containing the notation of an exercise session for middle aged and old men after six months of regular training (thrice weekly). The usefulness of the above notation sheet is comparable to that of the staff notation upon which an conductor of an orchestra relies in directing his players. By allowing identification and specification of each activity phase, its timing, number of repetitions, duration, quality of execution and other components of practical relevance, the training schedule under reference can be ubiquitously repeated, standardized, analyzed and evaluated. In the study mentioned (Fig. 49A), the physiological equivalent of the physical performance achievement shown in the graphic pattern was a statistically significant lowering of resting systolic and diastolic blood pressure of normal subjects and of subjects with essential hypertension. (A detailed description of the method of notation will be included in a publication *Exercise and Hypertension,* currently in preparation.)

FIGURE 50. The acquisition of skill represents one of the three great categorical aims of physical training in schools. Skill is the most educable facet of human efficiency, due to the presence of highly differentiated parietal lobes in man. The parietal lobes are the great mediator between his mental images and his motor actions. Skill is acquired through sustained effort directed toward the long-term goal of attaining a great variety of clearly designed objectives. In the development through training of "complex" body skills—in contrast to the "fine" skills which depend upon the use of the hands only—combinations of running activities with the manipulation of objects occupies an important part. The above picture shows a high school girl during a medicine ball-obstacle-relay in which she must direct a heavy medicine ball in a slalom-like manner through precariously balanced "gates."

FIGURE 51. With the emergence of a science of sports many remnants of esthetically repulsive, medically contraindicated and socially inexcusable forms of "athletics" are destined to die out. The most typical example is boxing, the stated aim of which is to incapacitate the opponent by inflicting upon him injuries, many of them severe, most of them irreversible, not a few fatal. Disgusting scenes like the one shown above are now brought into millions of homes by television without consideration being given to psychological harm thus caused. A special language has been introduced to camouflage serious clinical states brought about by the blunt injuries in the ring, such as "knock out," "groggy," "punch drunk," and many others. In several countries boxing has been banned and those associated with it rendered liable to criminal prosecution. (For a detailed account of the neuropsychiatric sequelae of pugilism, see Jokl, *The Medical Aspects of Boxing,* Pretoria, S. Africa, 1941.)

Physiology of course is not the proper discipline to dwell upon "good" and "bad." To show the need for the inclusion of criteria of a qualitative nature in the study of the subject, attention is drawn to the danger of the contemporary sports movement degenerating into a circus affair, with professional "athletics," some of them of doubtful import, determining its image as conveyed to the public by our media of mass communication. One of the most deplorable examples in this context is the continued toleration in our society of boxing (Fig. 51).

Sherrington on the Nature of "Knowledge"

Sherrington has emphasized that our bodies are the one part of nature of which we have "direct" knowledge. One may well add that there are grades of such direct knowledge, and that the differentiation of skill which comes with sustained practice facilitates its expansion. The average city dweller can no longer acquire such knowledge. Susan Langer has pointed out that town people today know nothing of the earth's productivity; that they do not know the sunrise and rarely notice when the sun sets.

> Ask them what phase the moon is in or when the tide in the harbor is high, and likely as not they cannot answer. Seed time and harvest are nothing to them. The power of nature is not felt by them as a reality. Realities are to them the motors that run elevators and cars, or the steady feed of water and gas through the mains, and of electricity over the wires, or the crates of foodstuffs that arrive by night, or the concrete and brick, bright steel and dingy woodwork that take the place of earth and waterside and sheltering roof for them. Nature as man has always known it, he knows no more.

However, man's capacity to acquire skill continues to place into his hands a key which can open doors to a world of values inside himself by acquainting him with and bringing under his control happenings in the world around him. The skilled motor act, Sherrington wrote, "seems to clinch the distinction between self and non-self. The doer's doings affirm the self."

REFERENCES

1. Asmussen, Erling: Growth and athletic performance. *FIEP Bull, 4*:22-25, 1964.
2. Asmussen, E., and Heeboll-Nielson, K.: Isometric strength of adult men and women. Comm Test Observ Inst Danish Nat Ass Infantile Paralysis, No. 11, 1961.
3. Astrand, P. O.: Human physical fitness with special reference to age and sex. *Physiol Rev, 36*(No. 3):307-335, 1956.
4. Astrand, P. O.: Physiological aspects on cross country skiing at high altitudes. *J Sport Med, 3*:51-53, 1963.
5. Astrand, P.; Engstrom, L.; Eriksson, B.; Karlberg, P.; Nylander, I.; Saltin, B.; and Thoren, C.: Girl Swimmers. *Acta Paediat Stockholm Suppl. 147*:1-75, 1963.
6. Bakwin, H., and McLaughlin, S. M.: Secular increase in height. Is the end in sight? *Lancet, 2*:1195-1196, 1964.
7. Bakonyi, Ferenc: Wirkung der Körpererziehung und des Sportes auf die geselligen Beziehungen der Schüler. *Proc Res Seminar Int Council Sport Phys Ed,* UNESCO. Budapest, Hungary.
8. Behnke, A. L.; Feen, B. G., and Welham, W. C.: The specific gravity of healthy men. *JAMA, 118*:7, Feb. 14, 1942.
9. Blachowski, S.: Polish research on psychology of sport. In *International Research in Sport and Physical Education,* E. Jokl and E. Simon (Eds.). Springfield, Thomas, pp. 109-122.
10. Chang, K. S. F.; Chan, S. T.; Low, W. D., and Ng, C. K.: Climate and conception rates in Hong Kong. *Hum Biol, 35*(No. 3):366-376, 1963.
11. Christensen, E. H.: Beiträge zur Physiologie schwerer körperlicher Arbeit. *Arbeitsphysiol, 5*:463.
12. Cussen, J.: Medical report on Melbourne Olympic games. *Proc Brit Ass Sport Med,* London, pp. 6-11.
13. Davie, James S.: The use of a college mental hygiene clinic. *Yale Stud Med, 4*(No.2):74-83, 1956.
14. Dickinson, E. R.; Piddington, M. J., and Brain, T.: Project Olympics, U.S. Army research and development group. *Schweiz Sportmed, 14*: 305-313, 1966.
15. Espenshade, Anna: Motor performance in adolescence including the study of relationships with measures of physical growth and maturity. *Soc Res Child Dev,* 1940.
16. Finski, O.; Janota, J.; Ciesla, W.; Jawerski, J.; Ulatowski, T., and Karolczak, B.: Physical fitness, level of learning results and physical development of growth from three Warsaw schools in relation to the

number of hours of physical education in the syllabus. *Wychowanie Fizyczne Sport, 3*:573-580, 1959.

17. Food and Agriculture Organization of the United Nations. *Ann Rep,* 1963.
18. Frucht, A. H., and Jokl, E.: Parabolic extrapolation of olympic performance growth since 1900. *J Sport Med, 4*:142-153, 1964.
19. Hanley, Daniel F.: Report of interview. Medicine in Sports. *Newsletter,* Rystan, Mt. Vernon, N.Y.
20. Henderson, Y., and Haggard, H. W.: The maximum of human power. *Amer J Physiol, 72*:264, 1925.
21. Hill, A. V.: The physiological basis of athletic records. *Lancet, 2*:481-486, 1925.
22. Hill, A. V.: *Muscular Movement in Man.* New York, McGraw-Hill, 1927.
23. Ikai, Michio: Training effect on muscular endurance. *Proc Int Cong Sport Sci,* Tokyo.
24. Jokl, Ernst: Menarche, growth and physical efficiency. *Nature, 157*:195, 1946.
25. Jokl, Ernst: Medical research in physical education in South Africa. *Res Quart, 20*(No.1):88-109, 1949.
26. Jokl, Ernst: *Alter und Leistung.* Berlin, Springer Verlag, 1954.
27. Jokl, E.; Karvonen, M.; Kihlberg, J.; Koskela, A., and Noro, L.: *Sports in the Cultural Pattern of the World (A Study of the Olympic Games 1952 at Helsinki).* Helsinki, Inst. Occupational Health, 1956.
28. Jokl, Ernst: *Physiology of Exercise.* Springfield, Thomas, 1964, pp. 43-47.
29. Jokl, Ernst: 'The effect of altitude on athletic performance,' and 'On disposition after running.' In *International Research in Sport and Physical Education,* E. Jokl and E. Simon (Eds.). Springfield, Thomas, 1964b, pp. 361-369 and 682-688.
30. Kobes, Frank: West Point studies concerning the predictive value of initial physical performance levels of freshmen. In *Symposium: What is Sportsmedicine?* 12th Ann Meeting Amer Coll Sportsmed, Dallas.
31. Kretschmer, Ernst: *Körperbau und Charakter,* 25th ed., W. Kretschmer (Ed.). Berlin, Springer, 1967.
32. Kruk-Olpinski, W., quoted by Blachowski, S.: Polish research on psychology of sport. In *International Research in Sport and Physical Education,* E. Jokl and E. Simon (Eds.). Springfield, Thomas, 1964, pp. 109-122.
33. Mellerowicz, H., and Hansen, G.: Sauerstoffkapazität und andere spiroergometrische Maximalwerte der Ruder-Olympiasiegel im Vierer mit St. vom Berliner Ruderclub. *Sportarzt Sportmedizin,* pp. 188-191.
34. Mischev, Dimiter: Age and Olympic performances. *Bull Bulgarian Nat Olympic Comm, 9*:23-26, 1966.
35. Pieter, Jozef: Testy uzdolnien ruchowych. *Roczniki Kultury Fizycznej, 1*(No.1):7-60.

36. Reeves, J. T.; Jokl, P., and Cohn, J. E.: Performance of olympic runners at altitudes of 7,350 and 5,350 feet. *Amer Rev Resp Dis, 92*(No.5): 813-816, Nov. 1965.

37. Robinson, S.; Edwards, H. T., and Dill, D. B.: New records in human power. *Science, 85*:409-410, 1937.

38. Russel, J.: *World Population and World Food Supply*. London, Allen and Unwin, 1954.

39. Russell, W. Ritchie: Paralytic poliomyelitis. The early symptoms and the effect of physical activity on the course of the disease. *Brit Med J*, Mar. 19, 1949, pp. 465-471.

40. Sheldon, W. H.; Stevens, S. S., and Tucker, W. B.: *The Varieties of Human Physique*. New York, Harper, 1940.

41. Sherrington, Sir Charles: *Man on His Nature*. Cambridge, Cambridge U.P., 1940.

43. Straus, Erwin: Memory traces. In *Phenomenological Psychology*. New York, Basic Books, 1966.

43. Tanner, J. M.: *The Physique of the Olympic Athlete*. London, Allen and Unwin, 1964.

44. Turnprüfung bei der Rekrutierung, 1962. Beiträge zur Schweizerischen Statistik, Heft 35, Bern, 1966.

45. Wittich, G.: Psychosomatische Untersuchungen zur Bewegungstherapie bei Herzkreislaufneurosen. Verhandlg. d. Deutschen Gesellschaft f. Kreislaufforschung, Soziosomatik der Kreislaufkrankheiten 32. Tagung, 1966, 154-188, (Steinkopff, Darmstadt).

46. Woytinski, W. S., and Woytinski, E. S.: *World Population and World Production*. New York, Twentieth Century, 1952.

47. Zelenka, W.: Unsere Erfahrungen mit der Auswahl und Leistungskontrolle jugendlicher Fussballspieler. *Sportarzt Sportzmedizin,* Jan. 1967, pp. 25-29.

NAME INDEX

SUBJECT INDEX

G

H

I

K

L

M

N

O

P